Best in Health !

Carter Freeman

For information contact:

Front Porch Press
1619 Weltin
Orlando, FL 32803

SECOND PRINTING
ISBN 0-97448291-9

Printed in the USA

Join G. Porter Freeman online at www.bodyforlife.com

This is the second printing of this little book... the first printing was slap full of mistakes! It is the first book I have written and boy oh boy there were some misspelled words and punctuation errors and words left out and on and on. Thank goodness I didn't print but a few hundred copies. Maybe we can sell through them quickly, or sail through them quickly, either way. See what I mean? It has been a real learning experience. I wrote the book on my own and published it on my own and edited most of it on my own. I paid for every bit of it on my own and now, I must stand up and accept responsibility for the mistakes, on my own. One of the many words I misspelled was EAISEST (easiest)...I know how to spell "discipline" and "character" but don't know how to spell easiest... must be a moral there somewhere.

Its like getting your health back if you have been unhealthy or starting your Life over after a big setback. You might make a few mistakes along the way. I am taking a dose of my own medicine here when I preach to get back up and go at it again. Fail fast and move on. I know a lot of people who got married and divorced. Then they each married someone else and got it right the second time. That's kinda what I hope happens here. I bet I did it better the second time.

Anyway, most of the mistakes should be corrected. Lord I hope so. If there are still some mistakes, I'm sorry. It is a book about Life, not an English lesson. Read it for the message, not the grade. There might still be a misspelled word in here, but you will have to read the book to find out...

I appreciate you giving me a second chance to make it right. I hope you give your health a second chance and get it right the first time.....

— *Porter*

FINALLY**FIT** at 50

Down-Home Advice for
Transforming Your Body & Life

Porter Freeman
"Since 1949"

—Dedication—

At 10:30 this morning I got the news that my mother has died. I have never been so sad or so lonesome. I don't know what to do. She hasn't been well the last few years, and I knew this day was inevitable. Still, there is no compensation for the words spoken in that phone call.

I wish so much that my mother had taken better care of herself. If she had just improved her eating, done a little exercise and maybe dropped a few pounds, there is a good chance she could have stayed here a little while longer. That probably wasn't going to happen—she was from the Deep South, and her habits were formed a long time ago. I'm not sure if all that buttered corn bread and mashed potatoes, ham and golden-fried chicken did her much good in the long run.

Today I would give everything I have and all that I am ever going to have to hear her say, "I love you." I would give back all the parties and good times to see her walk through the kitchen one more time. It's too late.

She was so very proud of me being one of the Champions in the first Body-*for*-LIFE Transformation Challenge. She was happy I got out of the bar business and came to work for EAS. She was most proud of me going on the Jefferson County (Colorado) Sheriff's Department. She was thankful I turned my life around. I wish she had changed hers a little.

This book is about life, not death, so this is a good place to ask you to do me a favor while we are both still here. No matter who your parents are, they gave you one gift that is irreplaceable: They gave you life itself. Parents are human, and sometimes they make mistakes, but nevertheless—you are alive today because of them. None of the greatest men or women who ever lived could have done anything without being born. This is the favor: If your parents are no longer here, bow your head and close your eyes for a moment and simply say, "Thank you, mother, and thank you, father." I think they will hear you. If they are alive, put down this book and call them and say, "Thank you." You have the most precious gift on this earth from them: You are alive!

I will forever miss my mother. She wasn't perfect and neither was I, but she was my only mother, and I was her only son. We had each other. Now that's gone forever. Please, please, please… if you can call your parents, and if you can encourage them to improve their health, do it today. Do it before it's too late. I will be happy to write them a letter if you want me to.

I must live the rest of my life continuing to make her proud of me. She will know every time I help someone improve his or her health and quality of life. We owe our best effort to our parents and to ourselves. My mom won't hear me say, "I love you, mother," anymore (except in prayer), but maybe yours is still able to hear you, so why don't you go tell her? Now all I can do is write, "Good bye, mother… I love you and will miss you, and I thank you for my chance at life. I will see you in eternity."

Your son,
Porter

—Acknowledgments—

Here I sit in the book store again. My notebook on the table, cup of coffee to my left and possibly the most difficult task of the day, in front of me. This afternoon I am going to try and thank some of the people who had a hand in improving and quite possible saving my Life. Lord help me!

How do you tell so many people you appreciate your Life back? Just like the 84 day Body-*for*-LIFE Challenge I took in 1997, I'm going to give it my best shot. Here we go.

Thank you to my Mother and Father, Ruth Broussard and Galen Freeman. They gave me the most precious gift on this earth, they gave me Life. To my wonderful sister Collette Clark, who blamed me for all the mischief we got caught doing until I wised up to her in about the 3rd grade. I love you Collette. Thanks to my Grandparents and all my pals and buddies through grade school. Those are the best memories of all. On to the present.

Somewhere in this book you will read about my boss back in 1997. His name is Gene Dupont. He continues to inspire me to this day. Thank you Gene for the "time" to get to the gym. Also to my roommate Jim McCain. He held the parties down to a roar so I could get some sleep during the 84 days. He is a Marine and a good man. Thank the Lord he subscribed to Muscle Media back in 97, or I would have never known about Body-*for*-LIFE. There are a lot of others that helped along the way. Jimmy Tinder and Randy Silvernell. They would cover my shift at midnight or 1:00am so I could get to the gym for an hour. Believe me, it was a team effort. The list goes on and on but I don't have the paper and you don't have the time to meet them all.

Allow me to mention one or two more. Bobby Dixon, a true Champion who has the patience of Solomon. Joey Vincent Neratka, a guy who taught me the real meaning of the word "value". He is one of the smartest people I have met in my Life. Sgt. Steve Grossi of the PAPD. He was a hero long before 9-11 and has proven to be a hero since 9-11. A special thank you to David Kennedy. David was an editor at Muscle Media and worked directly with me for all those Freeman's Word and several articles that changed my Life. I had never written anything other than drink orders or speeding tickets before they turned me over to David. Now I have written a book. He went with me and Jeff Kundert to Vietnam and helped me explain how Jeff showed the world he wasn't a quitter 30 years ago. David walked with me through the World Trade Center and helped me make a pitiful attempt at saying good bye to those Heroes. Thank you David, you are a fine young man and can evidently do the impossible.

Let me wrap this up. These last two are going to be the easiest to write but the most difficult to explain.

If I were to get married and have a son, I would want him to be a lot like Eric Shrieves. He has been my pal and best friend for about 30 years. Eric owns several qualities that I think we all strive for yet continue to come up short time and again. We are human. He is honest to a fault. He tells you the truth. How often do you get that in a normal day? His word is stronger then iron. His yes is yes and his no means no. He cares deeply about everyone he comes in contact with. He cares if they succeed or if they fail. He gives his all and ask nothing in return. No gimmicks, no bait and switch, no smoke and mirrors, no BS. If you want to change your Life, go see Eric. If it is your lucky day, he just might say, "Let's do it." I wouldn't be here without his help. Thank you Eric.

Finally I want to say a few words about a fellow named Bill Phillips. I met Bill for the first time in February of 1997. He magically appeared uninvited in my bedroom about 3:00am one morning. He showed up in a magazine article talking about a Lamborghini and 50,000 dollars and some sort of a 12 week contest. He stood at the foot of my bed and asked me if I was really, really, really the 47 year old, 264 pound lifeless fat beached whale slob that I had become? Was I honestly intentionally throwing my Life away, or was there a true champion under those gallons of beer and pounds of lard? He politely ask if I was the real Porter Freeman, or an ant farmer? He finished his appearance by asking if I planned to continue throwing my Life away or was I ready to take control and regain my health? Then he disappeared. It was left up to me to find the answer.

Thank you Bill Phillips. Thank you for helping me and Eric save my Life. What can I say or write that could possible show my appreciation? There is no answer to that one. How do you thank someone for your Life? I guess the only thing to do is keep living my healthy Life and do all I can to help others get well. That's it! The way to repay Bill and Eric and my parents is to continue keeping the 60 pounds of fat off me for the rest of my Life. Its been 8 years and I haven't gone back to my old used to be. Thank you Bill, I'm glad I read your article and got a second chance. Please keep doing what your doing, there are still a lot of Porter Freeman's out there.

—Contents—
Part 1: Changing Your Mind
Foreword: The way I see it…

Part 2: Changing Your Body

Part 3: Staying the Course

—Foreword—
The way I see it...

As I write this I am somewhere over America, between Orlando and Denver. We were scheduled to leave Orlando at 10:30 a.m., but there was a mechanical problem in the cockpit, and the nice, safe crew from United Airlines needed three hours to correct the problem. We didn't take off until 1:30 p.m. That's okay with me—I would rather walk from Orlando to Denver than be unsafe. Thank you, United.

It's about 2:15 p.m., and we were just served a quick lunch on this three-hour flight. I had water and a great cup of Starbuck's coffee. Then the lunch tray came. It was a large cheeseburger with lettuce, tomato, onion and pickle. There was also a bag of cheese-flavored potato chips and two cookies. They were two large cookies.

Now here is what this whole book is about: I had absolutely no choice in, or control over, the time the flight left Orlando. The kind people at United, who know way more about airplanes and air safety, were completely in charge of that. I could have ranted, raved, jumped up and down, but this plane wasn't leaving until it was safe and sound and the people in control were ready to leave.

Smart idea.

What I *did* have control of was whether or not I ate the lunch they offered me. The charming folks around me ate every bite! On the other hand, I took the bread and cheese off the burger, put the lettuce and tomato on it and ate half of it with a fork. I chose not to have the chips and cookies. That was my choice. I was in control.

Some things in this life we will have absolutely no say so in. Some things (very few) we will have absolutely all the say so in. I couldn't do a thing in this world about the wiring in this plane. But I and I alone have absolutely all the say so in what I cram down my throat. I am in control of what I chew and swallow while I'm on this plane. Just like United controls what goes in their plane, I control what goes in my body. Now, you and you alone have complete control over what goes in *your* body. Next, you, and only you, control if you do or if you don't exercise.

That's what this book is going to be about—Choice, Control and Transformation. It's been seven years since I dropped over 70 pounds of unhealthy fat and added 10 pounds of muscle. This transformation was done in just 84 days. My choice and the results of my choice are documented in a pretty good video called *Body of Work*. The guy who made the video also wrote a bestselling book called Body-*for*-LIFE. He was kind enough to put me in both of them. Thank you, Bill Phillips. More about him later.

I don't want to waste your time, and I sure don't want to waste your money. If you are happy with your body, and everything in your life is just right, read no further. I can't do a thing for you.

Oh, but on the other hand, if you want out of the "comfort of your misery," then read on. I changed my life forever. I've lived each day since then and have never been sorry or hungry. I made the change from 260 pounds to less than 200 pounds. Seven wonderful years of FREEDOM! If you want to be free, you can and *will* get it. If you don't want to be free, that's fine. Return the book back and spend your money on something else—it's *your* choice. I made *my* choice and, personally, I couldn't *ever* go back to sitting around waiting to die.

If you need some help, some ideas, some good old-fashioned, down-home advice, read on. Like that lunch an hour ago, it's a matter of choice. This won't be a "how to" book; there are a lot of good ones already out there. This is a "how in the hell did I get to be unhealthy and then get better book." It's an inventory of the lessons I've learned throughout my life's trials, tribulations and triumphs. In this book, there'll be no talk about the best fad diets, fat-burner pills or quick fixes—no, just the raw, cutting-edge truth about what you need to do to take control again. What you need to do to get out of the rut. What you need to do to turn around your body and life for the better. So, without further rambling, here's *the way I see it...*

—Part One—
Changing Your Mind

—1—
The way I see it...
We all look and feel
about as good as we *decide* to

Let's begin this book with a little history quiz, just for the fun of it. Here are a few dates that should be easy to identify:

- July 4, 1776. Okay, everybody got that one?
- How about November 22, 1963? A very sad day for our country. We lost our president.
- November 9, 1989. The day the Berlin Wall came down.

Now, do you know what happened on October 21, 1949? Of course you don't. That's the day I came kicking and screaming into this world. It's a pretty important date to me and certainly was for my mother, but it's probably not as important to you or your mother as *your* birthday is.

It's a funny thing about dates—when they have some special meaning to us, they remain important throughout our lives, regardless of whether they mean anything to anyone else.

February 12, 1997. As far as I know, that day isn't written in any history book. It was probably just an average day for most Americans.

But what happened that day changed my life forever. I declared war on my fat. That was the day I *decided* to go from the couch to the bench—the weight bench, that is. There came a second in a minute in that early-morning hour when my fat, tired, old body said "ENOUGH!" For those of you who might not know my story, allow me to share...

One sunny afternoon in February 1997, I drove to the friendly Publix grocery mart on Colonial Drive in beautiful Orlando, Florida. Being a single guy, I could have walked through the store blindfolded and done my shopping. As a creature of habit, I bought the same things every time. I circled the store, loading my cart with beer, barbeque chicken, lunchmeat, bacon, eggs, a box of whatever cereal had the most color in it, and more cold beer.

On this particular occasion, I did something out of the ordinary. Just beyond the checkout counter, right by the front door, there was a scale, free for anyone to step on. There's no good reason why on this trip I took the time to step on the scale, but I did.

When the needle quit moving, my first thought was to report the broken scale to management. Probably so many kids had jumped up and down on it the springs were about to come off. I stepped off the scale and waited for the needle to go back to zero, then I stepped back on. It was still broken—the needle bounced straight back to 264 pounds.

Being 6 feet tall and fairly big boned, I figured I weighed

about 225. There was no way in heaven or on this earth that I was 264 pounds—*impossible*. It bothered me enough that the next day I put on a pair of shorts, a T-shirt and flip-flops, got in my car and drove back to Publix's. I stepped on the scale, and it went right to the raw, cold, unbridled truth—*260 pounds*.

February 1997, Porter Freeman, 47 years old, supervising night clubs, making a good living, great roommate, good friends, pretty girlfriend, having barbeques every week, drinking plenty of cold beer, oblivious to the fact that I had somehow managed to become a human pig.

I guess the Lord or someone of greater power heard me scream. A few days later a roommate dropped a copy of some fitness magazine on the cocktail table at our apartment and said I should read this article in it. He had never asked me in the two years we had been roommates to read anything, so I said I would.

Okay, this is where the story really begins. I went to work that night and did my usual routine. Four or five cups of coffee and handfuls of popcorn and pretzels. I probably had a club sandwich or personal pizza or something, too. Whatever I ate it was washed down with more coffee or diet soda. At around 9 p.m. on most nights, I would leave the club and check on the other clubs. At the time I was supervising three clubs, and one had a small restaurant in it. By 10 p.m. I would head for one of the local greasy spoons and eat like there was no tomorrow. Barbeque was my favorite.

Anyway, this particular night I went back to work with enough barbeque in me to feed a small army. I drank and socialized with the customers. I did it night after night after night. I didn't get falling-down drunk—I just partied and had a good time. I never drove when I drank because I lived half a block from one of the clubs. Of course, that was the club I always closed at night because I could walk home. Beer and bourbon, beer and bourbon, one after the other. Does this sound at all like maybe a pattern you might be falling into? Maybe it isn't booze in your case—maybe it's sweets or fast food or cigarettes or the television. Whatever the case, what we might have in common is the "rut." The way I see it, the only difference between a rut and a grave is the depth of the hole. And by this time, I had dug myself into a pretty deep hole—eating badly, drinking too many beers, lying on the sofa watching sports on TV instead of participating in them.

On with the story. This particular night, or by this time morning, I walked home, took off my coat and tie, put my gun on the dresser (closing up a bar at 3 a.m. can get dangerous sometimes, so one of us always carried a gun). I walked into the kitchen and grabbed another cold beer and a bowl of potato chips and plopped down on my bed. Before I got undressed, I remembered the article I promised to read, so I got up, walked to the living room and got the magazine. Now I remember all of this in exact detail, and I promise you this: If it happens to you, and I pray it does, you will remember the exact day and hour and minute and second and everything around you when you are born again on this earth. I don't mean like a religious thing—I mean like the retaking of your life.

I stuffed a handful of chips into my mouth and took a long

draw off that cold beer and opened the magazine to the article. I didn't really want to read it, but I'm a man of my word, so I started to read. There was a picture of some muscled-up guy on the cover standing next to a red sports car. I thought it was an article about a car. That didn't make a lot of sense, but what the hell—nothing makes a lot of sense when you're still up at 3 a.m. drinking.

The article was written by some guy named Bill Phillips, and he was going on and on about this contest he was having. He wrote he was going to give away his $256,000 red Lamborghini Diablo and add another $50,000, blah, blah, blah. I'm reading and the whole time thinking, "Yeah, then Ed McMahon and the Publisher's Clearinghouse Prize Patrol are going to show up and knock on my door, too."

There I sat, eating chips and drinking cold beer, hoping to hurry and finish the article. The whole plan behind the article was a contest where you take 12 weeks and get in your best-possible shape. People from all corners of the country could enter. Whoever did the best job would win the car and money. This guy Phillips made it sound great and that anyone in America could win, and I didn't believe a word of it.

I was almost at the end of the article when Bill quit begging me to get healthy and changed gears. He had been trying to convince everyone to enter his contest, pleading his case for good health, when all of a sudden, in the last paragraph, he said something like, "You've got nothing to lose and everything to gain. Fame, cash, a new car, a healthy body. If winning a Lamborghini and $50,000 can't motivate you, there is nothing I can do to help you. You're just dead, and you ought to *go start an ant farm or something!*"

Talk about a slap across the face. It was like Bill Phillips was standing right there in my room, at 4 o'clock in the morning, pointing his finger at me saying, "Porter, you big fat ass—how in the world did you let yourself get in such terrible shape? Is this who you *really* are? If so… *you might as well go start an ant farm!*"

I got so mad at that moment I wanted to hit him. I shouted out loud, "You son of a $#@&*! I'll show you!"

Who in the hell was he to come into my house at this early-morning hour, uninvited, and tell me I was a dead ant farmer? He didn't know me. He had no right to talk to me like that just because he offered me $300,000 to shape up. The nerve!

Let's review. It's February 12, 1997. I live in beautiful Orlando, Florida, have a great boss, making a good salary, have a pretty girlfriend, have the best friends a fellow could ask for, and I'm weighing in at a cool 260 pounds and 33 percent bodyfat. That's 85 pounds of pure lard I'm hauling around on my 6-foot frame. Let's continue…

It's almost 4 a.m., I'm munching on chips, drinking a cold beer, and some guy's ghost is in my room telling me I'm a dead ant farmer. Now I've been a Southern Baptist all my life (not an especially good one, but one nonetheless), and I don't really believe in ghosts, but something very strange was happening. He disappeared as quickly as he appeared. There I sat, alone, with this challenge in front of me and a bowl of chips and a half-finished beer.

Long story short, right then and there, I made a *conscious decision* to change my life. I was finally fed up with being fed all the time. Just fed, fed, fed.

I shut the magazine, threw the chips in the trash and finished the beer. I wasn't going to waste a good beer, and I wanted to finish it because it was the last one. I quit drinking. The next morning, I got up, didn't brush my teeth, didn't make my pot of coffee, didn't turn on the television, didn't do any of the things I had done every morning for the last 10 years.

What I did do was pick up the phone and call my pal Eric Shrieves. Eric was the manager of a gym in Orlando, and when he answered, I asked him two questions: Are you gonna be there? He said yes; then I asked him if I could come see him. He said yes to that, too. He probably thought I was coming to borrow money.

I guess it was about 80 degrees outside that day, and I remember putting on a long-sleeve sweatshirt and sweatpants. I had on a ball cap and sunglasses. I was covered from head to toe when I walked into his gym. Now that I look back, I was just trying to hide all my fat in a gym with a bunch of fit hard bodies everywhere. I didn't care—I was still mad and embarrassed for the first time, and I was going to see Eric and do something about it come hell or high water.

I marched into the gym, threw the magazine on the counter and said, "I want to do this!" He picked up the article, looked it over, put the magazine down, looked me square in the eye and said the three most important words of my life up to that point:

"Let's do it!"

In the following three months, I dropped 74 pounds of fat and gained much more than just muscle—I had more strength and energy than I'd had in my entire life, and even better than that, I had regained what I knew was my true character.

I'm confident and on track now, but I'll never forget where I once was. I know bad habits wait on us forever. They don't ever go away. They will always be there, just around the corner, lurking and looking for an opening. If you're addicted to food or alcohol or cigarettes or even the wrong person in your life, if you've got a bad habit of any kind, I don't think it just "disappears." If you stop setting goals for your future, if you start living in the moment again, that's when those bad habits will push their way back into your life.

Those 12 weeks—and the months and years that have passed since then—taught me a lesson that I now try to teach anyone and everyone who will listen:

Anyone can do what I, and thousands of others, have done. You *can* reshape your body and create a better, brighter future. But you need to take that essential first step—*you need to make that conscious decision to change.*

I made that decision on February 12, 1997. That date may not mean anything to you, but it's a day I will <u>never</u> forget—it's the day this Freeman became a "Free Man"!

What's today's date? This can be the day *you* mark in your memory as the day you made the decision to change your life for the better—the day when you declared war on your unhealthy lifestyle. This *very moment*, you can make the commitment to allow yourself to break free from the "comfort of your misery."

You can win this war. You can win it one battle at a time until the enemy screams in defeat. Close your eyes and picture yourself as Teddy Roosevelt charging up San Juan or maybe Potato Pancake Hill, fork drawn, defeating fat at every turn. Winning battle after battle against cigarettes or alcohol or unhealthy food. Getting ribbons on your dress uniform for bravery—for freedom! Can you see it? Can you picture yourself standing in victory 12 weeks from today?

Do I sound silly? Maybe. Do you think I'm trying to be cute? I'm not. On my tombstone, it could read, "Born October 21, 1949. Reborn February 12, 1997." The truth is, I was the walking dead at 260 pounds. I was losing the battle and was miserable in my poor health. I wasn't even in the fight.

Bad habits and choices were attacking me from all sides, and I just sat there and didn't do anything but encourage defeat. That was right up until I *decided* to make a change. Then it was war.

If I had not made that decision, my epitaph would be: "October 21, 1949… He never fought the war. He gave in to poor habits, bad choices and had little or no self-control. The fat had character, and Porter didn't. He was comfortable in his misery."

This is my plea to you—please, please, *please* allow yourself to break free from the comfort of your misery. Make that *decision*. Get up and fight! Win the little battles—one at a time. You can go to the gym, or you can watch a sitcom on TV. You can lose a few more battles and start next week or next month. But remember, losing little battles adds up to losing the war.

All you have to do is get up, circle the date on the calendar, and declare war on your bad habits. In three months, you will stand in victory, having defeated poor health and changed your life forever. Then it will be your duty, just like mine, to help others break free from the comfort of their misery.

P.S. If you want to know who won the Lamborghini, the amazing answer is revealed in that film I mentioned earlier, called *Body of Work*. It's been seven years since that movie came out, but I bet you could find a copy on eBay or at your local movie rental. Maybe a friend of yours has a copy—over a million people and counting have seen this inspiring, true story about winning. I hope someday you have the opportunity to see it, if you haven't already. I really believe *Body of Work* has inspired more people to make that *decision* to make a change than any other.

P.P.S. A lot has happened since my transformation. I am no longer supervisor of nightclubs. I'm the Director of the Body-*for*-LIFE Challenge—yes, the very same competition that offered the car and money in 1997. This year, we aren't giving away another Lamborghini—insurance is a tad steep—but we do still have the Body-*for*-LIFE Million Dollar Challenge. To enter, all you have to do is log onto **BodyforLIFE.com** and follow the directions. It's easy to enter, and *anyone* can win. Don't believe me? Prove me wrong.

—2—
The way I see it…
We're either in control or out of it;
there's no middle ground

This book isn't just about me. I'm not that interesting. It's a book about *us*. You and me. That *is* pretty interesting. I would like to write a few things about how I did it (the transformation), but more importantly, *why* I did it. What was it I did? *I took control.* The way I see it, you are going to be one of two places every minute of your life. You are going to be either *in* control or *out* of it. No middle ground.

I've heard people say, "Well, he was almost dead." There's no such thing as "almost dead." We're either alive or not, no in between. We're going to inhale on this earth and exhale in eternity. No gray area there. We've all heard people say, "Well, she's a little bit pregnant." What? There's no such thing as "a little bit pregnant." You either are or you're not. You might be three minutes pregnant or three months pregnant, but you either are or you're not. Same thing with control—you're either in control or out of it. See if this applies to you. If it does, then maybe the steps

I took will work for you. Neither I, nor anyone else, can make the change for you. It's something you have to do alone. What can happen is someone can care but just stand by. Someone can tell you how they did it; nonetheless, you have to do the work. Now let's boil this thing down to gravy—low-fat gravy.

I was in love with the wrong person. She was the right girl, but the wrong person. I bet there are a few women reading this wondering if I'm talking about them. The answer is yes. Maybe that's not your problem, but it was a huge part of mine. She was in pretty good shape, but she ate poorly. It was part of my lifestyle to eat breakfast at 3 o'clock in the morning. I was in the bar business and didn't get off work until then. She would eat whatever, and I would get the eggs (cooked in butter), bacon, hash browns, toast, jelly, sausage links and pancakes. Why did I do that? Part of the reason was because she wanted to go out and eat. She was in the bar business also. First problem: The person I was with most of the time didn't practice or follow healthy habits. As a matter of fact, my family didn't practice healthy eating habits, ever, in my life.

My grandfather was a preacher for 68 years, and I certainly remember when there was a funeral, people would bring covered dishes to the church or to his house after the service. Every kind of unhealthy, fat-laden, vein-clogging, fried, high-cholesterol food and dessert you could think of. They meant well, but if we had eaten all that food, it would have the direct result of having us join the dearly departed sooner. I grew up learning to eat everything on a pig but the squeal (and it was encouraged). I swear to whatever you hold sacred, I have sat down with four other people to a table covered with enough food to feed a hoard of Vikings attacking England. When the knives and forks were through flying, nothing was left.

The other side of the coin was the drinking. I won't get longwinded about alcohol because that was just the drink of choice for me. It might be soda pop, sweetened ice tea or buttermilk for you. Mine was alcohol. For me it was beer and bourbon. And let me tell you, there was plenty of it. That gal I was mentioning earlier was partial to scotch. I've had four or five jobs in my life, but for the most part I was in the bar and restaurant business. I'm sure it was just an excuse, but I drank. I did it professionally. If you have a bar and a couple of your friends come in and want to buy you a drink, that's more money in the till. They might be celebrating a job promotion or a job completion. Some sort of special occasion that would warrant a $300 bottle of champagne. And other times there was just no reason at all. Just go down to the bar to have another person to talk with. Regardless of the reason, I drank. The raw, cutting-edge truth is I liked to drink. Plenty of times I paid for the drinks, and plenty of times I picked up the tab. I drank for the sales and for the hell of it. I enjoyed drinking with my pals and my girlfriend. Mine was booze; what's yours?

Is it soda pop? With hundreds of grams of sugar, does all that soda keep the fat on you? Is it the ice cream milkshakes you have with the cheeseburger everyday that's keeping the fat on you? What are you drinking and eating for fun that's killing you? I'm not going to harp and scream about calories and sugar and fat and carbohydrates—everything we eat has some of each. But, I beg you, find out what's in all those things you're eating before you continue to swallow them. For example, one milkshake and a piece of fried chicken with biscuits—oh, nevermind. I said I wouldn't harp, and I won't. If you want to know what you're putting in your body, you make the effort to find out. I did, and I know the information is out there. Remember, no one but you can do the work. Take one day and find the food value of everything you eat that day. It's pretty amazing.

Let's review. I was eating and drinking badly, and I was doing it with the wrong person. Does any of this sound familiar? Are you eating wrong? Are you eating the wrong food, at the wrong time, in the wrong amount, with the wrong people? Are you drinking wrong? Wrong amount, wrong time and with the wrong people? Are these people leading you in the wrong direction, and do they *really* have your best interest at heart? Do they have a different set of goals than you do? How will you ever succeed with the wrong person? You won't—I didn't; it just can't be done.

On February 12, 1997, I was 47 years old, 260 pounds, 200/130 blood pressure and drinking all the time. If you're any age, overweight or rail thin, if your blood pressure is way too high or way too low and if you're abusing your health with sugar, alcohol, food or drugs, or even the wrong person, then stop— you're dead wrong. Stop, right now on this spot. Right now. I remember the actual second I got back in control. February 12, 1997, I stopped trying to kill myself. You can commit suicide a lot of ways. A fork is one way. A bottle of liquor is another. Sometimes just not caring is another. Some folks do it all at once, get it over with, finished in a hurry. Other folks take their time killing themselves. I was the latter.

I took my own sweet time. I did it one drink at a time, one less heart beat at a time, one more 3 a.m. breakfast of pancakes, bacon and eggs, just to rush home and go straight to bed so that I could get up the next morning and have lots of energy to rush to my grave some more. One of my favorite sayings is, "The difference between a rut and the grave is the depth." You can get out of whatever rut you are in, but none of us is getting out of the grave.

Let's see if we can get you, or someone you love, out of that rut. A lot of people helped me. I'm going to talk about them later. I owe them all equally in my success. They helped me. Is there anything I can do to help you? Do you recognize anything in this chapter? I had to find out where I was before I could move in the right direction—towards freedom. You have to do the same thing. What has caused you, and is continuing to cause you, to be unhealthy? If you know the answer and do not want to change anything, then this is the end of the book for you. If you *do* want to change, draw the line in the sand right now. This is going to be the starting point.

Listen, I have thought about this a long time, and I believe there are only two things in this world you have total control over. First are your religious beliefs and second is what you eat. No one or anything can make you believe in a God or religion that doesn't feel right for you. Nobody but you can say "yes" or "no" to junk food. You're the one who controls these choices. Being unhealthy by choice is the only condition where you are both the cause and the cure. You play both parts in this: You are the doctor and the patient.

You don't always marry the one who is your real sweetheart. You don't always get the promotion you want, or even the job you want. When I'm older and sitting in a rocking chair, my life almost finished, I think I will know whom I've always loved. It didn't work out. I'm sure we'll all have some regrets and some sorrows. Probably that's just part of life. But, where my soul is going after I die and whether or not I fit in the casket is wholly and totally up to me. The same applies to you. If you want to be found drunk in a gutter somewhere, you certainly can. If you want to die from an overdose, that's your choice, too. Want your heart to explode and have them carry you out of an office building in the middle of the afternoon? Keep on doing what you're doing. Nobody is going to cram those cookies down your throat or that straw up your nose but you, and nobody is going to make you continue or quit but you. Please turn your health around, please! Trust me on this one, being healthy is better. I should know. Read on!

—3—
The way I see it...
A bite of the bait ain't
worth the pain of the hook

Do you think a doctor has to have the disease in order to treat it? I don't. Think a preacher has to die in order to preside over a funeral? Of course not! There is an endless list of expertise that doesn't include participation. You can study about a subject, read all sorts of books about it, talk with people who've done it, get a degree in a subject and become an expert in that field. Being healthy *isn't* one of them. To be an expert, you have to *do it*. You have to do the work.

Think about this: Nobody is in jail for what they did—they're there because they got caught. I'm so happy you can't see the mistakes I've made in my life. The list stretches from Golden, Colorado, to Atlanta, Georgia. I never did anything *really* bad or against the law, but I did do things that were wrong. There's a big difference. Everything legal isn't right, and everything right isn't legal. I'm sorry for all the things I did that weren't right. They may have been legal; they just weren't always right. I got away with some of them, and I got caught other times. How about you? Aren't you glad everybody doesn't know your innermost secrets? Did you ever do something wrong that nobody knows about? We all have.

Let's see if I can make a point here. I've thought about it and there are two things we can't hide no matter how hard we try. You can "fake" an education for a little while, or you can act interested when you're really not, and you can even pretend to be in love when it's the furthest thing from your mind and heart. There is an endless list of what we will get away with, or have gotten away with, for a long time.

You still can't hide two things: your eventual state of health and your addiction. These two will creep, slip, slide, stumble, rush, roar and burst into plain view. Poor health and addiction are like blocks of ice that travel in front of us, all the time. The more we feed them, the dirtier they become and the more people begin to notice them. You can see through ice in the beginning, but when it starts to catch dust, dirt and cracks, it's not so transparent. We might think other people don't notice the change, but they do.

If someone you know becomes rail-thin and turns the color of paste, have they really concealed it? Of course not. Something is wrong; their health is slipping away. The same applies to a person who gains weight. If you see someone who is fit and trim, then six months later they have gained 30 pounds in their waist and butt, something's wrong. I've lost a grandparent to cancer. I know the difference between the choice of selected poor health and the consequences of an unavoidable disease that was diagnosed, treated and succumbed to. Big, big difference. You can't hide the loss of your health. You can cover it up, you can dress differently, you can tan, you can use make-up, but you can't hide it. It's in your eyes and face. I knew someone who played a lot of sports to purposely hide bruises from another "sport." This person wore long-sleeve shirts to hide the bruises. Just remember that gloves don't hide a shackled hand. Poor health is eventually cured or discovered, one or the other. I hid mine, and I promise you again, being healthy is better.

I know bartenders who don't drink (not many), but there are a few in this world. There are people who make cigarettes who don't smoke, and some doctors who do. There are some overweight athletes and some underweight sports figures who have abused their health. I feel I have a right to write the next few lines. There's a song that goes, "I've got a right to sing the blues," and another one that says, "Any fool can sing the blues, not everybody can live with them." Therefore, I feel I'm 100 percent qualified to discuss addiction. It doesn't matter what the addiction is, if you've got it, it's got you. And when you beat it, you, too, will be a bonafide expert in it.

Did you ever hear anybody say, "I can quit anytime I want to… but I just don't want to"? I concur. You've got to want it. I'm not sure I can explain it… I'm not sure I can describe it… but when addiction gets its sweet, inviting, razor-sharp talons in your gut, it's real hard—no, hard isn't the right word. It's damn near *impossible* to get those ever-growing cravings out of your body.

Remember, *a bite of the bait ain't never worth the pain of the hook!* Don't you think if you could interview a fish that was being dragged out of the water into the boat, one that was desperately trying to spit out the hook, it would say, *"Son of a bitch, this isn't worth it! You can have your worm back!"* Unfortunately for that fish, it's too late. There has to be a moral here. First don't do it. Second, quit right now. Spit out the hook before you are rolled in salt and pepper and thrown into the pan.

Listen, I'm as guilty as anybody you know. I was addicted to probably the worst addiction possible. Among other things, I was addicted to a lazy, easy, do-nothing and just-existing lifestyle. I can't imagine a worse addiction. At least drug addicts have to make some sort of effort to get the drugs. I had to find a cold beer and a couch. I could eat whatever and however much of anything I wanted and wash it down with soda or beer or bourbon. I could eat at noon and again at 1 p.m. I had no boundaries. I've said it a hundred times: "I ate everything off a pig but the squeal." Pizza—I always got the second one 'cause it was only half-price. I thought, "You just can't pass up a money-saving deal like that."

"No rules" is exactly right, and instead of a blooming onion, I was a blooming idiot. No family, no real debt to worry about, good-paying job, just full-bore, slap-ass out of control. Sleep late if I wanted to, take a day off if I really wanted to, if I woke up with a hangover, I knew the previous night's sales were good. I had an excuse for everything, and it became a lifestyle. Or maybe it was an addictive *deathstyle*. Yeah, that's what it was. The only problem with doing nothing is you never know when you're through.

Listen, does this apply to you? Addiction is a monster that comes in different forms. The ONLY way to beat it is to choose to be somewhere else. You have to let it in the front door, or go to where it can be found, for it to work its magic.

Let me compare two of my addictions for you. One was a plate of grease-drenched pork barbeque with a bottle of bourbon. The other was a drop-dead gorgeous woman I knew. The first one weighed about 3 pounds and the other weighed about 120 pounds. One of them floated around on a plate with a piece of cornbread stuck in it and the other floated around in a tight skirt, with addiction stuck in the middle of it. The only thing they had in common was I couldn't say no to either of them. One was wrecking my health and the other was wrecking my nerves. I couldn't get enough of either of them.

Of course, it wasn't just the barbecue and bourbon, nor was it just the person. It was everything that went along with them. One plate of pork every now and then isn't going to hurt you or me. If I'd kissed her goodnight and then left, that wouldn't have hurt me either. It's the "over and over again" that leads to addiction. It's like seeing someone drowning and you try and try to save them. You get them closer and closer to the edge and closer and closer to being saved, and all of a sudden you're drowning like they are. You look behind you and notice they're swimming back to the deep water as hard as they can, to drown again. Finally when you both get to shore, they stop drowning just long enough to fix you a plate of barbecue and a six-pack.

I've got to tell you this story, please pay close attention. It may come in handy someday. This little scorpion is running through the forest, trying to get home before nightfall. He's young and scared of the dark and not really sure of his way. He comes to an opening in the forest and finds a big lake in front of his path. Far across the lake he can make out his home at the foot of a huge tree, but it's getting late and the little scorpion can't swim. The scorpion sits down at the water's edge and tries to think of what to do. He'll get lost trying to get around the lake and he can't swim. What to do, what to do?

Sitting about five feet in the water is a little frog watching the scorpion. The scorpion sees the little frog and says, "Mr. Frog, please help me. I need a ride across the lake, and I must get home before nightfall."

"No way," says Mr. Frog. "You'll sting me!"

"No I won't, I promise," said the little scorpion. "I need to get home, and if you will carry me on your back, I will make sure none of the other scorpions in the forest stings you either. I will tell them what you did, and you will be safe forever."

So Mr. Frog thought about it and came up with a good idea.

"Okay, Mr. Scorpion, here's what I'll do. I'll come into shore about halfway, and you come out till the water is up to your neck. I'll turn around and you jump out onto my back, okay?"

"Mr. Frog, I can't swim, will you please come closer?"

"No way," said the frog. "You come out and meet me, or no deal."

"Okay," said the scorpion, "I can't swim, but I have to get home—I have no other choice."

The little frog swims halfway to shore, and the scorpion wades out to where the water is just under his nose. Another inch and the scorpion will be underwater. The little frog backs up slowly, and the scorpion makes a final jump and grabs onto the little frog's back. The frog immediately begins to swim away. Off they both go headed across the lake. They're swimming along nicely, the frog is very confident, and the little scorpion is holding on for dear life. As they swim farther across the lake, the water gets darker, colder and deeper. The frog is very comfortable, but the passenger is holding on tighter and is more scared than ever before. Soon they're halfway across the lake and the water is darkest and deepest right where they are.

It's at this point when, all of a sudden, out of nowhere, the scorpion raises its poisonous tail and starts slamming it into the frog's side. Out comes the tail and back in again. Over and over the scorpion pumps all of its poison into the little frog. Finally the scorpion is completely out of poison and out of breath. The searing white-hot pain begins to devour the little frog and as he begins to go down in the middle of the lake, he comes face to face with the drowning scorpion. In his last breath the drowning frog asks the scorpion, "Why did you do it, now we are both going to die?"

And in his last dying breath, the little drowning scorpion said, "It's my nature."

When you get involved with something that has the potential to control you—when you find that you can no longer refuse the bait—remember the frog. At some point (the sooner the better) realize that you are becoming addicted to it. No matter what it is—food, drugs, alcohol, the wrong person, the wrong lifestyle, sugar, chocolate, money, sex, power, fame, whatever—spit it out before you can't spit it out. Remember, we said the difference between the rut and the grave is the depth. You can get out of a rut, you really *can*.

The problem is the longer you stay in a rut, the deeper it gets. You don't stand still in a rut because time is passing, and that alone makes you go deeper. I know you can get out; I did, and so have thousands of others. You and you alone have to want out. Honestly, I sometimes hurt because I can't find the words to weave you a rope to help you up. I swear I know what it feels like. I wrote in Bill Phillips' book Body-*for*-LIFE that some people feel like they're "living in hell." Do you think I got a divine vision one night and knew that? Or do you think that maybe I've lived it? I've been right where you are. I know it's hard, but I know with all my heart you can change. I also know you won't change if you don't want to.

I'm not trying to save a million people; I'm trying to tell you that *yes*, you can pull those hooks out. Anyone can. You can, you can, you can. "Will you?" is the question. Make your choice based on these truths: It's not that you can't change your life, and it's not that freedom isn't out there waiting; these are truths—and it's also the truth that it's you making the choice. Nothing more.

—4—
The way I see it…
You can never lie to
yourself and get away with it

Today was a very sad day for me. I had to say good-bye to
one of my best friends. We've all had to do that at some point
in our lives, and if you haven't, you probably will someday. It's a
part of life. I can think of nothing good about his passing except
I had the privilege of knowing him.

I miss him dearly and wish so very much he was here. I want
to talk to him and laugh with him and listen to his stories of
long ago. He had seen quite a bit in his life, and I ended each
visit a better man for spending a little time with him. If there's
anything positive about this day, it's that I at least knew him and
can share some of his wisdom with you. This is going to tie in
with your health, so stay with me.

My friend's name was Harvey Miller. That probably doesn't
mean much to you, but watch and see if you don't know someone
who resembles him in some way. He passed into eternity, and
now his ashes are in the Indian River. He loved Florida and has

gone back to the land he loved. Maybe it's just me, but I think a small part of Harvey is in every blade of grass, every palm tree, and every drop of Florida water.

I have to think that no matter where I am in Florida, Harvey will be somewhere nearby. He went back to the ground, and if I am in a mango grove or a dark swamp, I know he's there. I know he's wherever I am, in my heart.

Trust me, I sure love my father, and I love my stepfather—there will never be any more like them in my life. I love my friends, both new and old ones. I've got male friends and female friends; friends don't have to have gender. I never understood why some people don't want their boyfriend or girlfriend to have a buddy of the other sex. Insecurity, I guess. I've got both kinds of friends. A friend is a friend, end of subject. It doesn't matter what race or religion or gender they are.

If you're in an accident and find yourself in the emergency room and need a pint of blood, are you going to ask, "Is it male blood or is it female blood?" Are you going to ask, "Is it American blood or is it European blood?" All blood is red, and when you need it, the only thing that matters is if it's clean and available. That's kinda how I see my pals. Not color or religion or anything else, but are they there? My real friends have always been there, and I will always be there for my real friends.

Harvey fell into the older male category. He was born 35 years before me and was getting a little long in the tooth when I met him. Picture a long, tall, white-haired fellow who walked and talked real slow. He sort of looked over his glasses at you and had an "I know what the hell you're thinking smile." I'm sure in the 25 years I knew him, I never saw him in a hurry, and he only raised his voice once. Not at me.

Maybe we should all be polygraph examiners. That's what Harvey was. Some of that occupation must have spilled over into his brain because Harvey could pretty much talk to someone and know if they were telling the truth. There are probably a lot of detectives who've been on the job for years who can do the same thing.

Of course, Harvey had done that also. He'd been a detective with the Florida Beverage Department back when good 'ole boys were lying about selling and making illegal moonshine whiskey. He told me a lot of stories about sloshing around in the swamps and on back roads of Florida during the 50's and 60's. He was prepared for the Beverage Agent job because before that, he had romped and stomped all over North and South Carolina in the Marines and then on to Okinawa during WW II.

He loved his children and wife, and he was crazy about girls (one at a time, I think). He loved his family and friends right up until his last day. I liked that about him. The other thing he loved was the truth. I don't know if he always told it, but he loved it, and he sure knew it when he heard it. Not sure how many polygraphs and voice-stress tests Harvey administered, but it was probably in the thousands. I won't debate if polygraphs are right or wrong. I've taken a dozen of them, and I know when I was lying and when I wasn't. So did Harvey. He never discussed a particular exam with me, but once in a while, after a long grueling exam, he would look over his glasses and grin. "He didn't fool me," Harvey would say. "I knew the son of a @#$%& was guilty as Adam." I never knew Harvey to be wrong. Harvey didn't care if someone was guilty or not. That wasn't the point. It never came into the equation. His singular goal was the truth, nothing more, nothing less. All Harvey did was report if the examinee was truthful or not truthful. End of subject.

If asked, I don't think Harvey was a saint. Who is? He was rough as a dry cob and very set in his ways. Whether he was right or wrong, he had principles, and he stuck to them no matter the cost. You always knew where you stood with Harvey, and he always told the truth. God, I'm gonna miss him!

Where does all this lead you and me? To this point. I wouldn't ask you to do something I haven't done. So here goes... *what is the truth with you?*

Sitting on the side of my bed one night, drinking my sixth or seventh beer of the day, chewing handfuls of chips and pretzels, weighing 260 pounds, I got a face full of Harvey Miller truth; I was a self-induced SLOB!

I can just imagine a polygraph with Harvey. It would go like this...

Harvey: Are you dangerously unhealthy?
Answer: Yes.
Harvey: Do your friends accept you like this?
Answer: Yes.
Harvey: Are you going to spend the rest of your life like this?
Answer: This is where you, or someone you love, has to say yes or no.

See, in this polygraph, you get to play both parts. You are the examiner and the examinee. Harvey is gone. He won't be giving any more exams. I do not know how to operate the polygraph instrument, or read the charts, so I don't know if you will be truthful or not. Oh, but on the other hand, you can ask this question: Am I going to stay on this unhealthy lifestyle?

You could have lied to Harvey, but he would have known it. You can lie to me; I will know the truth if you aren't changed in a couple of months, but you ain't ever going to be able to lie to yourself. You've got your own little polygraph built in. It's called a conscience. Every day that you stay a hostage to your own addictions, the answer is "yes." And every day that you do something to break those self-inflicted chains that bind and hinder you, the answer is "no." And every day that you do nothing, the answer is, "I just don't care."

The truth shall set you free. There's total freedom in truth. You don't have to say a word. In a few weeks everyone around you will know and see if you've told the truth. It shows. They can't help but notice a change.

I owe Harvey a lot. Late one night in February of 1997, sitting on the side of my bed, Bill Phillips asked me and all of America if I was an ant farmer. Somewhere in the pit of my 43-inch stomach, I saw Harvey Miller looking over his glasses and heard him ask, *"What's the truth?"*

This past weekend I flew a long way back to Florida to tell Harvey, "Good-bye." He would've done that for me. His daughter, Sally, was kind enough to allow me to visit her property and walk down to the river where Harvey's ashes went back to the Florida soil. God, that was sad for me. He's definitely gone, but the river keeps right on moving and the truth will live on forever.

So long, Harvey. The truth is, I miss you, but I know we will all see each other again one day.

Where is your truth? Who is the Harvey Miller in your life? Who is your friend or relative who pleaded, "Don't hurt yourself anymore"?

If you lie, some people might buy it, but you won't. We can lie to each other, but we can't lie to ourselves. I know, I know, of course we can lie to ourselves, but we know we're lying. That makes a big difference. We know we're lying. I knew I was a big, fat, lazy drunk; I just lied to everybody else. I dressed sharp and was always clean. I tipped big and had parties every weekend. Always a good excuse to drink and eat. I had a cutie of a girlfriend—had one or two to be truthful! Life was good. But oh, wait a minute! Late at night, when everyone was gone home or passed out, the truth, along with my addictions, was right there sitting on the couch with me. They never go home, they never take a day off, and are always ready when you are. Isn't that funny, I can think of three things you will never have to wait for: the truth, addiction and recovery. These three things start the second you let them in your life.

The truth isn't a car on a cold Colorado morning; you don't have to warm it up. It comes red hot and ready to go. All you have to do is tell it to yourself and then do something about it, or don't.

Let me tell you what to do with the addiction, food, drugs, booze, whatever. Set it on the living room cocktail table. After awhile, if you don't use it, you can set the addiction on the shelf. If you still haven't used it after awhile, you can take your bad habit and set it in the closet. You don't have to dust it or clean it in any way. It stays ready. Then if you can go a few weeks or months, whichever is the truth, you can set it in the basement or outside in a storage shed. Then after a few months or years, you can wrap chains around it and put a lock and key on it and bury it out in the backyard. It won't be dead, it never dies, but it will stay buried as long as you want it to. It will only come back out of the ground the day you go dig it up. I know, I buried two or three habits and addictions in my backyard. I chained them up and locked them away seven years ago. Not all the time, but sometimes, depending on where I am and what I'm doing, I can hear their hearts beat. They're not dead, they're just buried. It's completely my choice to leave them alone or go dig them up.

Right this second it's 6:20 a.m. on February 16. I'm at 29,000 feet somewhere over the Pacific Ocean. I'm on my way to New Zealand to visit old friends and make new ones. We have a new Grand Champion in New Zealand, and I could not be any more proud of him. It will be an honor to present him with his ring and EAS champion's jacket. Also the $25,000 don't hurt!

Anyway, a very strange thing just happened. This cabin was pitch black except for my reading light. There aren't many streetlights over the Pacific at this hour, and it was real dark and quiet on this plane. In an instant the entire cabin was washed with white and gold light. I mean it looked like a volcano. The crew hadn't done anything; they were asleep. I turned and looked out a window and realized it was the sun. It happened so fast; it was the daylight being cut on. I saw it happen from seat F-6, row 12. Harvey saw God throw the switch. That's the truth.

—5—
The way I see it…
With faith the size of a mustard seed, you can move mountains

It's Sunday morning, and I'm sitting in church. This won't be a long chapter. I'm going to start listening real soon to the sermon. The guy in the pulpit knows more about the subject than I do. I've learned to listen to and watch people who know more about the subject at hand than me. The preacher has devoted his life to this Christianity thing. He can teach me something. The question is, am I willing to learn it?

Here I sit, Sunday morning in God's house. That's my choice. Nobody drug me in here, and just like the gym, nobody is going to drag you in there. That will be your choice. I'll get about 45 minutes of instruction this morning, and I'll be a little closer to my salvation. I hope you do something today to get you a little closer to your salvation. And remember this: It doesn't matter what you wear or what shape you're in when you start. He remembered me and forgave me when I walked back in the church, and you are forgiven and get to start over in the gym. Just get started. Church is beginning. We'll talk later.

One hour later and the preacher was right on track. He talked about Matthew: 17. In plain old Porter Freeman terms, it says, If you have faith the size of a mustard seed, you can do anything. This is a good example. In the martial arts, when you break your first board, you will hear over and over: "See your hand or foot going through the wood. See it on the other side of whatever you are trying to break." That's nothing more than faith. You must *believe* you can do it.

Maybe you will get something out of this book—maybe not. Either way, you should at least meet a few people who do have faith. Look at what they did with limited ability. How did they enter and complete the Challenge and improve their life? They had *faith* they could, and they did. There are thousands of people who've overcome all sorts of limitations. You probably know someone who has let nothing stand in the way. I sure do.

Look at the best example I can think of, Helen Keller. I think it's an honor for me to even write her name. I couldn't do and haven't done anything compared to her accomplishments. All I did was stop acting like a pig; big deal. I quit eating like a starving water buffalo and quit being a professional drunk. Are you going to tell me you can't control your diet and exercise? I think you can... you are just as good a person as I am.

I can just imagine a conversation with Ms. Keller and me; it would go something like this...

Me: Ms. Keller, I really don't have time to exercise. I manage a couple of bars and have a lot of staff to schedule and product to buy. You understand?

Helen: Yes.

Me: You don't really understand. I have to drink when my buddies come by, and my girlfriend likes to eat after work. I just can't get to the gym and eat correctly.

Helen: Yes.

Me: You can't imagine the pressure put on me to not have a healthy lifestyle. I have to celebrate everybody's birthday at work. I can't turn down a drink, and what's dinner without a little dessert, and I just can't throw food away. Ms. Keller, you just don't understand!

Helen: Oh, I see.

She accomplished more in a single day than I have in a lifetime!

I'd like to introduce you to a friend of mine named Paul Sullivan from Phelps, Kentucky. Paul had been to a deacon's meeting and stopped to buy gas on his way home. He went in to pay the bill and walked in on a holdup. He walked in the gas station in 1990 and left on a stretcher, never to walk again—never. Does he think he will walk again? No. Does he think the loss of his legs was the end of him? No. Does being in a wheelchair stop Paul from working out religiously and helping other people to get in great shape? That wheelchair does not slow him down one bit.

Let's think about this for a minute. Paul stops to pay for gas, goes in and is stabbed in the back. He's paralyzed from the waist down, and he goes home and builds from scratch a gym from a shed in the backyard. He lets anyone come train there and doesn't charge one penny. If they want to donate a dollar, it helps pay the gym's heating bill in the winter. You can call it inspiration or you can call it determination or you can call it whatever you want to. I call it *faith*. Paul Sullivan has the faith that he can improve.

Let me share a few other examples of faith. There's a guy in Wisconsin and another one in Los Angeles who give me faith. Jeff Kundert and Joe Getherall found themselves in combat at a very young age. They were shot, hospitalized, shot again, wounded, blown up, and Jeff was crippled for life. Jeff can walk following numerous operations but only with the help of a cane or crutches. His legs are chewed up, torn apart, and, for the most part, were left in a jungle 30 years ago. Both of these men came home (finally) to become productive, exemplary citizens. Joe went on the LAPD for 28 years, got his Master's Degree, rose to the rank of Captain, and still teaches in law-enforcement academies. Jeff graduated minus the crutches and has a degree in health sciences. They overcame a lot. They are true Champions. A lot of people have had horrible experiences in their lives. We've all had to overcome some sort of difficulties, but there are a whole bunch of people with no excuses who don't have enough faith to make the sun set.

Let me tell you about another friend of mine named Vicky Magnum. She was a 1998 Body-*for*-LIFE Champion. Trust me on this one, she was a Champion long before 1998, and she will be a Champion long after I'm gone. I don't want to bring up bad subjects, but I got her permission to share this with you. She'll read this, but it won't remind her of sad occasions because she already thinks of them every day. Vicky's firstborn son was playing in a sandbox one day and a car ran a stop sign, jumped the curb, and killed her baby in front of her eyes. Her second son was fishing just off the shore one afternoon and was coming back in when he hit a stump or something in the lake and drowned. Vicky was on the shore. Vicky has had some form of cancer for the last 20 years.

It was mainly in her stomach, but for the most part has been cleared up. She will never pay her medical bills; she will never go one day without thinking of those precious children. She has a beautiful daughter and beautiful grandchildren. She is very protective of them.

Each morning Vicky wakes up, she wonders if her old nemesis, Mr. Cancer, will show back up. Yet she gets up, goes to work, smiles, tries more than anyone I know to help others and keeps her head up. She did the Challenge and won; you know why? She had faith she could do it. She wanted to improve her health and even if it was only an inch or a pound, she had faith (from somewhere) she could do it. She is a real Champion.

I have two distinct feelings when I'm around her: shame and awe. I'm ashamed of all the whining I've done in my life over unimportant crap, and I'm in constant awe of her outlook and attitude toward life. She's not a fool, she doesn't always see the silver lining, she knows she has a choice. She can give up, or she can face the day holding onto faith that somehow she will survive and do someone some good. Thank you, Vicky—you give all of us faith.

My last example is from a guy who doesn't want to be introduced. He doesn't want any recognition, and he doesn't think

54

what he did was any big deal. I think it was a real big deal. Some of the things he told me bounced around in my empty head for a long time. When I decided to do my 84-day transformation, the remarks he had made came roaring like a locomotive out of my memory. I got his permission to share them. You are more than welcome to them.

When he was 19 he was captured in Korea and became a prisoner of war for almost four years. There are a lot of stories like this in America, but this is his. You never know when you hold a door for someone or help someone, in some small way, who they are. You never know what price they may have paid defending you, themselves or this country. You never know, just in passing, whom you might be talking to. To look at this gentleman, you would have no idea what he has been through. If you didn't know Vicki Magnum and she stepped in front of you in a line, you might bite her head off. If you did know her, you would do well to let her in the front of the line. Not that Vicky would ever break in line, but you know what I'm talking about.

Anyway, my good friend finds himself in a POW camp, as a lot of Americans did. Now, my friend has a choice. He can give up and die or stay alive and try, try, try to escape. You and I can stay where we are or we can try to escape. He made a conscious decision early on that he would not die at the hand of the enemy. Not that they couldn't kill him, they could. That would be something he would have no control over, nor any say so in. What he *could* do was try to survive and then if they killed him, at least he didn't kill himself. Think about the power of that statement, if he died, they would have to kill him, he wasn't going to kill himself! Listen, if you've seen the *Body of Work* video, do you remember when I said, "I'm going to finish these 12 weeks or they're going to find me dead in the gym"? He taught me that. He did a little bit different Challenge than I did. He graduated from a four-year Challenge that should have been named the Life for Body! He had to follow a different set of rules. He had to stay alive, not freeze to death, eat mice, roaches, seaweed and insects and if lucky, on his "free day," his cheat meal was a bowl of rice with some worms in it. For four years I sat on my fat ass, complaining about reconstructive surgery, broken hands, a scoped shoulder and the whole time I was eating more in a week than he got in any one month in 1950. I had waitresses bringing me a menu, but 50 years ago he didn't have guards coming up to him wanting to know if he would like the #3 Special or the #6 Special for supper. He didn't get dessert with the day's "happy meal," and there was no happy hour.

I'm not beating myself up. I'm not going to run headfirst into a wall as some sort of redemption for not being a POW in Korea. I know my friend loves me and would never want me or you or anyone to go through what he and so many others had to endure. What I am going to do is try to stay healthy and stay away from bad habits. I owe him that.

He told me that during one of his escape attempts he caught a chicken and ate it raw. Problem was, animals don't pluck chickens; only humans would. The enemy found the feathers and knew he was nearby. He got caught and got a tremendous beating (the scars are still there), and of course his food was cut in half. Here I was trying to eat four double cheeseburgers at lunch because they were on sale for 99 cents apiece and wash it down with 47 grams of sugar and 40 grams of carbohydrates. Never, never, never again!

Here's the bottom line I will not forget him saying: "If I died, it was going to be their choice, not mine. I had faith I could make it if they didn't execute me."

After working a 17-hour day in beautiful Orlando, Florida, having five or six good nutritious meals, getting plenty of vitamins and EAS supplements, and having a hot cup of coffee, walking in the Steel Mill Gym at 2 or 3 a.m. pales in comparison to what he did. The one thing he and I had in common was this: We both had faith we could make it. I knew my 84 days would end, and he knew his challenge would end one way or the other.

Will you make it 84 days? Or will it be too much? Is 84 days too much? Probably like my imaginary conversation with Helen Keller, he would understand.

Do you remember when Bill Phillips wrote in the 1997 Challenge that if you were using excuses to not get healthy, you should go start an ant farm? I remember it. Get mad; get mad at me if you want to. Get mad at the bully who shoved you down in the third grade. Get mad at the girl who lied to your boyfriend and he left you for her. Show that person who dumped you, and broke your heart, that they made a mistake. Change your life, and they will want you back, except you might not want them as much anymore. Show the people in your office, church, social group or school that you are in control. Choose not to die on the vine, having never ripened to your full potential. Regardless of your age, education, regardless of anything, you can improve.

Do not dig your grave with a fork or spoon. Don't dig your grave with a straw or shot glass. There are plenty of people out there who get paid to dig it for you.

One last thing about the gentleman who was a POW for almost four years… he and I have one other thing in common, we both love my mother. I asked him if I could introduce him and he said it was up to me. His name is Roy Broussard, and he's my stepfather. Thank you, Roy, and thank you to all the veterans of all wars and peacetime. We are here because of all of you.

These people gave us the choice to choose the quality of life we will live from this moment on. I have faith you are living the quality of life that you want. If not, change it. It's been paid for.

—6—
The way I see it...
The difference between a rut and a grave is the depth.
You can get out of a rut; you ain't getting out of the grave

I initially wrote a chapter about this subject—about giving up—then tore it up. It certainly didn't fit into a book about getting healthy and living life, or whatever the hell this book is about. One lady said it was about my memories. Nothing could be any further from the truth. This book isn't about me; it's about everybody and some of the crap that happens to all of us. This book is about one or two ways to make life a little easier. I have to talk about my experiences because I didn't have yours, but I do think you will see where we have sewn a common thread.

For the good people who have thought about ending their life, this will be a great chapter. For those of us who have come really close to actually doing it, this will be a fantastic chapter. And for those of you who have done it and been successful, well… I guess this chapter is a little late.

We've all known someone who has finally had enough and

put an end to their misery. The list of my friends and associates who have ended their failures is long, and it saddens me to think about them. I say an end to their failures because it wasn't their successes that kept them going; it was their failures that ended it.

When I was a little boy, I had a paper route for a couple of months. My precious, tired, worn-out father got up at 4 a.m. and drove me the first few weeks until I learned the route and knew exactly where to go. It took exactly one morning to learn the difference between riding in Daddy's Buick and throwing papers out the window and having a couple hundred papers hanging around my pencil-thin neck and trying to pedal a bicycle on the route. Big, big difference.

For a young man in the sixth grade, having a few dollars in my pocket was well worth the aggravation of having to get up and throw papers those first few weeks. I was a big shot on Saturday morning at the movies and had plenty of money left over for hamburgers, donuts, sodas, model cars and whatever else I wanted. Life was good for me (although a little rough for my father) right up until the morning I had it "all on my own."

Still, the rewards outweighed the discomfort. That's an important point in life even today. Do the rewards outweigh the discomfort necessary to achieve them? You decide.

On with the story... the first morning I pedal all over town. On the way down a dirt road, I get right in the middle of a row of houses, and the biggest, meanest dog I've ever seen comes out of nowhere and tries to eat me. This son of a bitch looks like the illegitimate son of "Rin Tin Tin" and "King Kong"... I forgot about delivering any more papers (those people could watch TV or listen to the radio for all I cared) and pedaled like a mad man getting away from "White Fang!"

The next morning, I'm going along the same route and the "Son of Dracula" comes from the other direction. Same story… I'm no longer concerned about throwing papers. Now my life's goal is to grind that bicycle to safety. I'm grinding like crazy, and the dog is snapping at anything on me that's moving. Next morning, same thing. I was in that dog's territory, and he wasn't having any part of it. In his marble-sized brain, I was the enemy camp, and his one job in life was to chase me, catch me and eat me.

Hate became fear. That's another important point of this book. Hate becoming fear or vice versa—fear becoming hate. If nothing is done about one of them, then the other is sure to appear. Then eventually, they become one and the same. I started out fearing that dog, and then I began to hate him. I changed my entire route so I would throw that street last. I could pedal faster without many papers left to carry. Finally, the dog caught me and knocked me off my bicycle. All the papers were dirty, and I was scared for my life. I tried everything—Dad drove me down the street, and, of course, there was no dog. He didn't chase cars. I had no idea which house the dog belonged to and wasn't going to go door to door asking. I was already pretty unpopular with the customers.

One morning I cut a bamboo pole and tried to be Sir Lancelot. All the dog did was bite the pole. Then I filled a plastic squirt bottle with ammonia and was going to squirt "Rover" when he attacked. Have you ever tried to hit a moving target in the dark while pedaling a bicycle on a dirt road, with a squirt bottle? I did get off one squirt, which went directly down my pants and partially on the papers. I'm sure the noise that morning was me crying, but it sorta sounded like that dog laughing. I've owned and loved a lot of dogs since then, but never that breed. I refuse to.

After about six weeks of seeing this dog three or four times a week (and never knowing when it would appear), I quit the route. That was six weeks of living in fear and my hatred for that dog and that street increasing daily. I just couldn't take it anymore. The dog didn't come out every morning and that just made it even worse. I wore my pajamas under my pants every morning just in case Rover did chomp down on me. Enough was enough. I had to quit.

Maybe that's how people reach their end. Maybe that's how people stop the uncertainty—they quit. There is something in their life that causes a great deal of pain, fear, hurt or all three. This, like everything else in this book, is just my opinion, but I think a steady diet of trouble is better than a dose of pain once or twice a day and never knowing when it's coming. If you are like Paul Sullivan and live in a wheelchair, then you go to bed and wake up knowing that you can't walk. He has accomplished a lot from that chair, but what if he could walk and a couple of times a day his legs just give way for nothing? What if you went blind at different times during the day and there was no remedy for it? Would it be better to be blind all the time?

There has to be a tie-in here somewhere. You can put the

"hound from hell" label on whatever it is that waits for you in the dark, never knowing when it will attack.

What snarling, vicious, mean thing is causing you to seriously contemplate ending everything just to get a little relief? Do you feel like an apple seed trying to get out of the apple? There's just no way out. We've been real honest with each other so far, and there's no need to change now. I had one roommate who hanged himself and about six other friends who gave up and "quit." What would I give to go back and learn the identity of their demons? I would give anything.

Is it the cookies? Is it being lonesome? Is it the value you attach to other people's opinions of you? Is it the booze? Is it the dope? Is it porn? Is it some strange religion? Did someone walk out on you and love another? Are you convinced you will never get over it? You damn sure will! I came real close to throwing in the towel once. There's no explaining it, and if you've been there, you understand. Maybe you lost your job and all your money; maybe you loaned your best friend a lot of money and then never heard from him or her again. Guess what? There are new jobs and more money and new and better friends out there. There are, there are, there are! Maybe you think that you can't lose 100 pounds. Guess what? You can, you can, you can!

I didn't know how to deal with that dog when I was 12, and I lost my paper route. I'm a little smarter today, and I wouldn't let the dog cost me my job. Of course, we get smarter as we get older (at least we should), and, of course, I now drive a car instead of a bicycle. Nonetheless, the formula remains the same. Don't you dare throw away a perfectly good life and a perfectly good person just because a junkyard dog is chasing you down the road, trying to bite you.

Naturally, there are people who need serious medical help, and they should seek it. I'm talking about the "Porters" of this world who don't think there is a solution to their problems when there certainly is. Maybe I am completely off my rocker, but one more time, everything in my life improved when I got off my rocker and got healthy again.

I honestly believe that if you are getting in the gym, or at least doing some kind of exercise, you are going to start looking and feeling better. Think about that. If you are ready to "give up the ghost" and you then decide to do something to look and feel better, do you think you would be as likely to give up? I don't. All of your problems won't go away, but you will feel better about dealing with them. Isn't that what we are all looking for—a way to better deal with our problems? Think about having something each day that makes you feel a little better about yourself. Booze and cigarettes and dope and the wrong person and the wrong job doesn't make you feel better—it hurts! So if you do something to make yourself feel better, you will look better, and then guess what—the better you look and feel, the more confidence you have. Just like fear leads to hate and hate leads to some sort of escape, exercise and healthy eating leads to looking and feeling better and that leads to *freedom*.

It may be an inch at a time or a pound at a time or one less smoke or drink or date or double-goo cookie bomb at a time, but you can get well, if you start getting well. It's like a journey—half the distance is the first step.

I'm gonna tell you right now somebody on this earth, and several in heaven, love me. It might or might not be whom I wanted to love me, but somebody does. The good news for me is, the better I take care of myself and the more I try to take care of myself, the greater chance I have of more people caring about Porter.

The same applies to you! If you are in the gutter or in the White House, *someone* somewhere cares what happens to you. If your family has passed and your dog has died and everyone you know has gone and left you, then I put myself forward as a candidate to be your friend. If I am the one person left in this whole wide world who cares about you, then so be it. Now you want to get better and now there is some one who cares, and the one thing left to do is give it a try. At this point there is nothing left to lose.

My best childhood friend got up one morning and ate his father's gun. That's what he wanted to do, and he did it. I wish so much he hadn't done that. I wish so much I could have walked into that room and said something to prevent what happened. I had a high school sweetheart who put an end to it all, a few years after graduation. I have no idea why. These people had to be afraid of something or hate something, and they didn't know when it would come visit them. So, they made sure they weren't going to be home the next time it showed up.

Some folks think the savage dog is hiding under the bed or in the attic. Some think it's in the basement or the garage, it might be everywhere outside or just in the shadows. Maybe it waits in a lake or large group of people. Maybe this demon is in addiction or self-disapproval or rejection. NO IT ISN"T. It lives *within* us if it has any life at all. When I was at my worst, my attack dog lived inside of me, not on a country dirt road 40 years ago. I am the one who fed and nourished the dog. It wasn't real, and getting up so that I wasn't sitting on the leash anymore allowed the dog to run from me this time. Amazing, ain't it? Let's change it from "who let the dog out" to "you let the dog out."

Don't ever throw your life away because you don't think anyone loves you. Until you give every living human being on the face of this earth the opportunity to know you, how can you say nobody cares? You can't. Don't ever forget Vicky Mangum, Paul Sullivan or Jeff Kundert. There are three examples of people who found a reason to improve, and each of their lives improved with the reason. There are so many people who have looked suicide in the face and finally said, "Get the hell out of my way, I've got a reason to *live*."

Sometimes late at night and often depending on what sad song I'm listening to, I feel that warm blanket of eternal sleep falling over my shoulders. Sometimes when Ray Charles or Janis Joplin is moaning the blues in my ear, I cannot deny I think of a past time and missing someone so bad it hurts. I do visit that place on occasion. Nobody in his or her right mind wants to be alone or held captive or suffer all their life. No child or parent (and we are all one of those two) has ever gotten up out of the grave (except Lazareth). Ending your life is ending all possibility of improving it. I would hate to think I met eternity while at the lowest point of my existence. I want to go out on a happier note.

Everybody has felt failure and sadness and misery at one time or another. It's not the end. As long as the sun comes up and we wake up, we get another shot at turning our lives around. Maybe you and I will win the lottery next week, but one thing is for sure—we have to be alive to go play it. Maybe we stay alive to write a letter thanking someone for a bygone good deed they did for us. Maybe we stay alive to call our best friends and thank them for years of golden friendship. Maybe we live for those soldiers who didn't live so that we could. Maybe we honor those who have gone before us but not at their own hand while saving others. We have a thousand reasons to stay alive, and I promise you, if you improve your health and still don't see any relief from those hounds of horror, death will still be right there waiting patiently. He never goes away. Let him pick the day and date, not you.

If you are thinking about calling it a day or you know someone who is, I want you to do me this one favor. Postpone the event for a little short while. What possible difference could it make? Try doing something healthy for a few weeks—swimming or lifting weights or some sort of exercise. Eat four or five good nutritious meals for a few days and drink a few glasses of water. The absolute worst thing that can happen is you will look a lot better in the casket. Buy some new clothes or get a new hairstyle, try a new church or a new job, change a few things before you go. I will bet you this—you will start feeling better and looking better, and that mean old dog will "lose tooth" every day that you improve. Pretty soon, the dog is toothless, and there is no more fear and no more hate and no more loneliness. I don't know whom you are going to meet in the next week or month or year. I don't know when happiness and fame and fortune will show up, or if they ever will. I do have a pretty good idea of your social calendar from the grave. All your dance cards are going to be empty. You're better than that.

—7—
The way I see it…
You ain't never gonna find a
diamond in a goat's ass, so quit looking

I have no idea as I write this if an editor or whomever in America will publish this book. How could I know? I am still writing it. If you are reading it, then it somehow got to market. We'll see. Anyway, it's my book, so as Popeye would say, I am who I am! Here goes. Sorry if I offend anybody, I don't mean to. Remember in the original article about getting fit, Bill Phillips wrote that if you were out of shape, unhealthy, sitting around, you were "dead"; that you should go start an ant farm? Now that I think back about it, instead of writing a little insult in his article, he should have magically appeared in my room and choked me for wasting my life and health. I wasn't mad at him; I was finally mad at me, and something he said got me motivated enough to do something about it.

I don't want to insult you, but here goes: "You ain't gonna find a diamond in a goat's ass." Quit looking! I doubt there is one little pill or piece of equipment or bottle of oil or ointment that will make you look like the person who is selling it. Let's get crystal clear on this. Getting up to change the channel on the TV is better than no exercise at all. Walking to the corner drugstore to buy ice cream is better than driving. But nothing I know of will take the place of this formula: Try to apply a 70 percent nutritional approach with 20 percent resistance exercise—free weights, machines, bodyweight-resistance exercises (like chin-ups, push-ups, sit-ups, etc.)—and then include a sound 10 percent vitamins and nutritional supplements approach. You want honesty, here it is. You know where I work and that we provide supplements. I believe they are the best on the market, but they alone will not make you look like the people on the cover of a fitness magazine. There, is that enough truth for you? I used four or five of the supplements and still do. If I had simply included them in my daily life without changing my old habits and forming new ones, like working out regularly, performing "cardio" combined with intelligent eating, I would weigh about 340 pounds now.

Please let me know where the secret pill, wheel, wire or magic supplement is that can take the place of changing bad habits and putting forth some old-fashioned effort . I want to get me one!

I understand how some people sign up for this or that class or with this or that trainer then walk away disappointed when they inevitably fall short of their goals. Remember the famous quote, "Everybody is ready to carry the stool when it's time to move the piano." I just don't think there's an easy way out. You, you, *you* must do the work to get healthy. A good, honest trainer is wonderful; still, you must do the work. Neither Eric nor Bill lifted one weight for me. Neither of them ate one of my meals. Again, I had to do the work. One more time, there is no pill, no secret method, no once-a-week five-minute exercise that will pull pounds of fat off your butt and slap pounds of muscle on your calves, shoulders and chest. Don't start writing me letters. Any exercise is better than none, and doing any movement that you weren't doing is an improvement; home gyms can be as good and sometimes better than having to drive 20 miles to a gym. There are some great companies out there that have honest, caring people working for them who can design a program for your home, and if you apply yourself, you will look better than I do. You will still have to do the work. There's no easy way out of quicksand; you have to work. I read somewhere that, "The road to hell is paved with good intentions." Don't just say you're going to get in shape, don't just buy the gym belt, do the work!

Some people don't have to worry about what they eat or if they exercise. I'm very jealous of them. I'm not one of them. I know some guys who pull cable all day who could compete in the "Mr. World" competition. They use their muscles eight hours a day. Some jobs demand great physiques. Being a bartender isn't one of them. I know some bartenders who are in great shape, but they work out on a regular basis to stay that way.

Again, don't go looking for diamonds in a goat's rear-end—there ain't none in there. Find some weights somewhere; lift them, do some aerobics and watch what you eat. That's where the diamonds and gold are found.

—Part Two—
Changing Your Body

—8—
The way I see it…
You don't know where you're going if you don't know where you are

You don't know where you are going if you don't know where you are. There are so many times in this life when we have to tell little white lies. I've done it and so have you. We all have told them and are going to continue to tell them if we are going to interact with one another on this planet. I think we're intelligent enough to know the difference between not offending your 85-year-old grandmother concerning her dry biscuits and saying you've lost your wallet, when the truth is you lost your paycheck at the dog track. One is bending the truth just a little, and the other is a bald-faced lie. I would rather have died of thirst, which I nearly did, than tell my precious grandmother that her cooking got a "little rough" toward the end. She never knew those last few biscuits could have choked a whale in the deepest ocean. If this book is in the Library of Heaven, then I will have to explain that last statement. But that will be okay 'cause I will be with her, and it really won't matter.

Little baby lies or raw, cutting-edge truth? There are only two ways to find out. First, tonight when you take a shower, take a good long look in the mirror. If you are looking for someone who refuses to lie to you, never has lied to you and never will lie to you, it's Mr. Mirror. Then you will know one-half of where you are.

Mr. Mirror will tell you everything you used to be. He will accurately report everything you have eaten and all the exercise you have or have not done. He is more accurate than the most advanced computer on the market today. He won't tell you what you're going to be; he doesn't know. Only you do. He will say without bias, "This is everything you have done in the past." The mirror is one truth you cannot run from. You have to look at it everyday to see what happened the day before. You can't look in a mirror and see what is coming, only what has been. It is the best yardstick to measure your previous choices. A mirror is raw, cutting-edge truth. You have to face your face.

The second way to discover the truth is to get a physical. Get your blood pressure taken, get your cholesterol done, and have a bodyfat composition done. This is the other half of knowing where you're going because when the results come back from these tests, you really know where you are.

I won't go into all the ways we waste money. I don't have time, and it would take a John Deere tractor to pick this book up. We just waste money. I know I have. We buy things we don't need and we need things we don't buy. I was guilty as anybody. You need a physical. You may not like what the doctor tells you, but most likely it will be cutting-edge truth, not baby lies. If I wanted little white lies, my doctor could have said, "Porter, you're 6 feet tall, and your weight is under 300 pounds, that's great!" BABY LIES! The truth was 6 feet tall and 260 pounds, at 30 percent bodyfat. What do you weigh? What is the truth? Where are you on the road to recovery? How much are you contributing to the weight of the world?

Get your blood pressure taken. How hard does your heart have to work to get blood throughout your body to help keep all that fat alive? Have you ever watched a garden hose when the water is turned on? Turn the water on full blast and watch the hose go crazy, flopping all over the yard and completely out of control. Your heart is doing the very same thing. All the extra weight demands your heart beat harder; it's insane, and I was guilty of it for years. How stupid. I'm surprised people all over America didn't hear my heart beating. Blood pressure about 200/130. What an idiot I was. If you're rail thin because some fashion designer from Paris says you have to be in a size 1 this season, you are taxing your heart just as unnecessarily. When we starve ourselves to be in vogue, when we don't eat, we cannibalize lean muscle tissue to get necessary protein. We devour our own muscle. That's just as ridiculous as being overweight. More cutting-edge truth. Have a body composition done. How much of your body is lean tissue and how much is blubber? We're not sea lions trying to stay warm on the frozen tundra. People eat sea lions to stay alive at the North Pole. But, if you're not living in the North Pole, you probably don't need all that extra blubber on you. I should know, I lived in Orlando, Florida.

Now I admit I was a fat body in Orlando. Again I was wrong.

When I lost all that weight and moved to Colorado, I learned you could dress in layers of clothes and stay just as warm as a polar bear. Find out how much fat you are keeping stored in your body. Is it 10 percent, 20 percent, 30 percent, how much? How much do you need? Everybody will tell you something different. Who's right? You are. I don't know what's right for you; I only know what's right for me. I also know what's wrong for me, and I know I don't need 20 percent bodyfat at 200 pounds and 6 feet tall. That would be 40 pounds of fat. I don't need 40 pounds of fat unless I'm going to get evicted from my apartment and have to go live in the Rockies this winter. So, what is right for you? Do you live in Miami Beach? Do you need 40 pounds of fat there? Do you live in Seattle? You don't need 40 pounds of fat there, either. Let's review. Take a good, long, honest look in the mirror. Get a physical or at least get a bodyfat composition done. Get your heart rate measured. You will, if at all concerned, at least know where you are and most likely, where you're going. Go get the physical.

—9—
The way I see it…
There are 4 steps everyone must take to escape the comfort of their misery

What do I have to do or say to get you out of the comfort of your misery? That's exactly where I was in early 1997. I was comfortable wallowing in my misery. I had a decent car, I had a pretty girlfriend, and I had a lot of friends. I was fat and happy on the outside. But inside, *I was miserable.*

Are you happy? Are you *really* happy? Or, do you "appear" to be content with the world… while on the inside, things just aren't quite what they ought to be?

Neighbor, if that's where you are, then you are standing in my footprints. Like so many of my pals, I played the lottery in hopes of winning and throwing a really big party. It was, and continues to be, fun to sit around and pretend to be rich. Pretending is all that it was; none of us have won the thing yet. I didn't pretend to be in good shape or good health—I just didn't care. Somewhere I read the most unreliable man is one who just doesn't care. That wasn't me… I was very reliable. I cared about everything under the sun except the most important thing: me. My bills were paid on time; I still to this day have good credit. My clothes were cleaned and pressed, and I always was concerned about how I dressed. My hair was cut, and I was clean. My biggest concern was always my job. I was in the bar business and wanted every drink accounted for. I hired "shoppers" to go in the places I supervised and report to me any "hanky-panky" going on. I always believed my boss couldn't pay me if I wasn't making him money. I was a Notary and performed several marriages. Having been brought up in the church, I was honored to speak at several funerals. I cared about my word and wanted people to be able to (like it or not) know I was telling the truth. If there was a problem at work, I didn't hide from it. No matter what the problem was, my managers or the owner could always come to me, and we would find a solution. With all that said, I didn't give a tinker's damn about my health.

Did I just describe someone? Did I just describe you? Maybe I described someone you love. Did I just describe someone you know who cares about all their friends but will not take care of his- or herself? A person who is honest, hardworking, trustworthy but is ruining their life with drugs, liquor, food or tobacco? Are they getting proper nutrition, or too little nutrition? Do they work hard and bring home their money and go to church. Are they a good parent, husband or wife, grandparent or stepmom or stepdad? And are they killing themselves by not doing any exercise and going to bed drunk or stuffed or high? That was me a long time ago. Who is it now?

Two of the greatest personal joys I've had because of this

experience happened about two weeks apart, and they happened because I changed my life. A year or two ago, a lady named Cindy Homan wrote me and asked if I would consider coming to Raleigh, North Carolina, to speak to a group of Body-*for*-LIFE Transformation Challengers. This presentation was going to be held in the Unity Church of Raleigh. I politely refused. I didn't think I was ready to say anything in church. I've spoken to thousands of people, but the thought of saying one word from the pulpit scared me to death. I wasn't scared of Cindy or the preacher, Jack. I had drifted quite some distance from the church, and the thought of having to face the Lord froze me in my tracks. I honestly prayed about it and asked my best friend, Eric Shrieves, what to do. I finally went to Raleigh, and this is all I will say about it: The Lord did not forget me. He was waiting at the door of the church with open arms. Just as the mirror tells you all you have been, the Lord tells you all you can be. Today I am literally a "Free-man."

That was one experience; here is the next. We got invited to Franciscan University in Steubenville, Ohio. The school had a Wellness Fair, and I was one of the speakers. Now you think that over for a minute. I went from arguing with drunks in the parking lot of topless bars to giving my testimony at the Unity Church in Raleigh, North Carolina, then having the honor to speak to the student body at a University. Whew! Want to talk about changing your life? One more time, if I could do it, you can and *will* do it, also. That is, if you want to.

At Franciscan University, I looked in the eyes and faces of young people eager to do God's work to help their brothers and sisters. Anxious to go to the missionary fields and work every day to make this a better world. The men and women at the Unity Church were equally as dedicated to living productive, good lives. I don't know which experience was the most rewarding. It would be like saying which grandmother you love the best; you just can't put one above the other.

A note of thanks also to Keri Davies. Keri was part of the International Public Relations Department at EAS. Seeing her face in the congregation at both places and hearing her speak gave me a great deal of support. Thank you for going with me, Keri.

The very, very sad part of those two experiences was witnessing the poor health of several of the wonderful people in both Raleigh and Steubenville. There are some people in this world who take care of everybody else and for some unknown reason, don't care a bit about their *own* health. Some people had made a miraculous transformation and others continued to serve the Lord and their fellow man, but they chose to do it with a cigarette in their mouth and a 40-grams-of-sugar soda pop in their hand. One man of the cloth actually told me he was too busy helping save lives to take time for working out or to exercise. That would be like a doctor living in the emergency room, never going home or bathing, never taking time to eat or brush his teeth, because he might miss someone coming in on a stretcher. It's ridiculous. I heard excuses both places. "I've got to go to class, I also work at the hospital, and I visit the jails, and I have three children at home." And on and on and on and on. Excuses upon excuses. These two don't work, try two other excuses. Those don't work, try two more. When people run out of excuses, they can always fall back on my all-time favorite, "Oh Porter, you just don't understand!" That's my favorite because I had used it for years.

Smart, intelligent, good, caring people who are so comfortable in their misery that they won't change. Those are their choices and their consequences. I finally decided on February 12, 1997, to get in control of my life, when, in the early-morning hours, I shouted, "That's enough! I'll show Bill Phillips!" When that second in that moment came on that unforgettable morning, I made four rules and stuck to them like a duck on a June bug. They're my gift to anyone on this earth who wants out of the *comfort of their misery!*

1. **Want it**
2. **Make it a priority**
3. **Stop doing bad things to yourself**
4. **Start doing good things to yourself**

Four simple, easy rules, nothing earth-shattering or profound. I don't expect to be quoted for years to come; they won't be taught at some major university, and there won't be any discovery of a deep philosophical meaning behind these words. The two strongest words in this world are simply "yes" and "no." Do you want to get healthy? Yes or no.

These four simple rules apply to almost everything I do today. I'm sure you have rules or a creed you live by, and these four aren't the only boundaries I have, but when it comes to changing your health for the better, they can be instrumental in helping you become finally fit.

#1 Want it!

The first morning you get up and don't want to be healthier anymore, and you don't want to be fit, it's over. I racked my brain, the part not soaked in alcohol, that morning in 1997, and I couldn't get away from those two words: *Want it!* The "it" I wanted so much was to be in control again. I wanted to show Bill Phillips and the world I *could* be fit. I wanted to know "it" for myself. Sometimes marrying the prettiest girl is just good luck. And sometimes being successful in business is luck. We all know some rich people who were poor and some poor people who used to be rich. Remember, a silver dollar goes from hand to hand. Being fit and healthy is something a person with only a high school education or a Ph.D. can have. It all boils down to this: *Do you want it or not?*

At Franciscan University, I met students who had full schedules; some were far from home, some worked part-time jobs and were on a very tight budget. Nonetheless, they stuck with it because when it came to their education, they wanted it. I know people who spend three or four hours a week on the driving range to get their "iron game" down, simply because they want it. I have a friend in Orlando, Bobby Dixon, who spends hours in his martial arts school, practicing on the heavy bag and sharpening his skills. Why? Because he is a world-champion kickboxer, and when it comes to world championships, he wants it. *You gotta want it*—nothing more, nothing less. The day you wake up and say to yourself, "I don't want it anymore," then it's over. Don't waste your time. I'm not talking about wanting to take a day off; you know damn good and well what we're saying here. You've got to want it.

#2 Make it a priority

How do you make something a priority? Simple; attach a sense of value to it. People ask me, "How do you attach a sense of value to something?" I can't think of anything any more valuable than our health. For years I didn't understand that, or at least didn't accept it. I didn't put any value on my health. I was wrong, wrong, wrong! Look, if you have a tooth that hurts, and if you don't go to the dentist, sooner or later, you will probably lose that tooth. When that happens you might say, "So what? I've got 31 other teeth to chew with." Eventually another tooth gets chipped or decay sets in and now you're down to 30 teeth. You see where we're going with this? When all your teeth are gone and you can't eat an ear of corn and the only thing you can chew is a donut or bowl of mush, you either eat the mush or get false teeth to help you chew. Now, suppose we attach some value to our teeth while we have them and start taking care of them today. We won't need to have false ones, and then we can eat more than just a bowl of mush when we're older.

I was trying to explain this to a gentleman on the phone one day and he just wasn't getting it. He was lost somewhere between priority and value. Maybe it was my accent, I don't know. Regardless, I hope I don't offend anyone, but I'm going to write exactly what I finally told him, and I apologize in advance.

Here goes…

"Suppose you're driving your car and come to a stop sign. That's normal, it happens every day. You come to a full stop, look both ways, and before you proceed through the intersection, your car backfires. In your rearview mirror you see a small puff of smoke come from underneath the car and you continue driving. You make a mental note of it and maybe think about pulling into a service station later to make sure everything is A-okay.

"Now let's suppose you come to the same stop sign, look both ways, then begin to cross the intersection. Same backfire, same puff of smoke, but this time huge, roaring flames are shooting up from underneath the car. These flames are raging through the seats, your pants have caught fire and the interior is filling up with smoke. All of a sudden getting across the street is not as important as getting your ass out of the car and away from it. Your destination is no longer the priority, and you have now attached a new 'sense of value' to your balls."

He didn't say anything for a minute, and then he said, "Thank you, Porter, I got it." Then he hung up. Ask someone who has had an unexpected heart attack if all of a sudden things in this life don't change in terms of value. I was "on fire" in 1997 and didn't get it… how stupid I was! Fat, blood pressure out of sight, drinking like I was a fraternity pledge. Are you on fire and don't know it? I was comfortable and burning up. Please don't let another day go by so that if and when they take you to the emergency room, the doctors have to say, "It's too late, they should have gotten out sooner." Today is the day to get the hell out of that car before you burn up or burn out, whichever comes first.

Don't think you can put down that bottle, the wrong person or a couple of packs of smokes a day? Don't think you can go all day without a candy bar or a soda pop or something unhealthy to eat? If you don't put it down, it will put you down. What won't kill will fatten for the kill. Somebody ought to invent a beer called "one more." Because everybody in the world who doesn't have any control always says, "Oh, I think I'll just have one more." Want to quit smoking? Just have one more. Want to quit drinking, eating crap, and wasting your life with the wrong people? Just have one more! For 20 years I was married to "One More." Now I date a couple of different people, they are "No Thank You," "Bad Choice," "I'm Driving," and my favorite new girl is "Ms. In-Control." I may marry her.

The priority is *you*. Attach a sense of value to yourself. What are you worth? *You* are the most important person in *your* life. Make *your* health *your* priority. Don't listen to Pierre from Paris tell you how skinny you should be. The latest fashion has nothing to do with your health. Being skinny is as bad as being fat. When it comes to your health, you be the fashion leader, not the follower.

#3 Stop doing bad things to yourself

You don't think something like obsessive gambling can ruin your health? Think again. I have a friend who'll be glad to tell you it damn sure does. I watched a boss of mine lose everything at the track. He would ignore his work and spend his time charting a race sheet. He would volunteer to work a second shift and then not show up. He answered the phone at work one night by asking, "What's the score?" Lucky for him it was me calling.

He cussed and his face turned bright red when his team lost. He would borrow from the employees and then lost all respect from and all control over them. All he did was smoke, drink, gamble, and try to beat the odds. He seldom did. Don't you think his health was directly affected by his obsessive gambling? I know it was. Have a little bet sometimes, it's fun. Dad and I play a dollar or two on the lottery each week and then make that "we're still in the poor house" call to each other the following Monday morning. I travel a good bit, and if I don't buy my one lottery ticket this week, it will be all right. I know Dad will get one, and we will laugh when it does or doesn't come in.

I went to Las Vegas last year and I lost nearly $20. I was with Bill Phillips' brother, Shawn, and I had a big time. I laughed, went night clubbing, ate intelligently, drank in moderation and exercised while I was there. Who won, Las Vegas or me? We both did; my old boss didn't. I don't know what happened to him. He got fired, and I never saw him again. No matter what the addiction, if the return is on the down side, stop doing it.

Addiction… now we're getting down to the real nitty-gritty dirt floor. Another one of my pals, Joey Vincent Neratka, told me one of the smartest things I've ever heard in my life. He said, "Addiction is a patient lover; it will wait on you to get out of the grave." Truer words were never spoken. If you are hooked on something and give it up, I don't care how much time goes by, the addiction is still waiting, lurking, looking for an opening, ready to ease back into your life. How do I know this? Because I was addicted to the wrong person for a hell of a long time. She was the right woman, but the wrong person. Big difference there. Good lord she was, and still is beautiful, but the wrong person. Does this ring a familiar bell with you? Not that you know her, but that you recognize the addiction. What are you addicted to? It's hell, ain't it? When I think of her today, all I can think of is, "A bite of the bait was *not* worth the pain of the hook."

If you're trying to get healthy, both mentally and physically, and you're involved with the wrong people, find out what those people weigh because that's exactly how much weight you need to lose immediately. You might be going to the gym, but while you're there, if you're wondering and worrying about what they're doing, or the argument you had on the way out the door, you're not focused on your health. I swear to whatever you hold sacred, I've packed my gym bag, put on my sweats and have gotten into an argument with "that woman" on the phone, and by the time we hung up, I went to a bar instead of the gym. I've planned to work out at the karate school and not gone just to avoid an argument. If you find yourself ignoring your exercise and going to bad places and doing wrong things to appease him or her, stop, stop, and STOP! If someone in your life isn't trying to promote you and your health, they can't be doing anything but holding you back. Why in the world did I let someone feed me a steady diet of negativity for five minutes, much less for five years? Was it love? Is it love? Hell no, it's addiction! We were in a rut and, remember, the difference between a rut and a grave is the depth! You can get out of a rut; do you want to?

I repeat, *stop doing bad things to yourself.* I saw a great T-shirt once... I was in Daytona Beach and a guy walked into a bar wearing it. I've never found it or seen it since, but I'm sure there will be thousands of them out there once this is read. It was a black T-shirt and written on the front, in white letters for all to see, it read: *Rules for Life.* I just realized this was 25 years ago, before Body-*for*-LIFE. Still, it's kinda the same thing. Here goes...

Don't eat at a place named Mom's.
Don't play cards with a guy named Doc.
Don't shoot pool with a fellow whose first name is a town.
Don't sleep with anyone who has more trouble than you.

That's pretty good advice: Keep negative people out of your life. It has got to be horrible for your health.

The last thing we will speak of on Rule 3 is about what we eat. It's beyond me how we can sue the tobacco companies and jump on the bandwagon to make them pay, when we promote places that encourage, invite, entice and reward us (and our children) to clog our hearts and arteries with dinners that contain 50 or 60 or more grams of fat per serving. I don't get it. I, along with thousands of Americans, watched the court cases and read the papers concerning the tobacco industry trials. I'll go along with whatever the jury decided; they heard the evidence, and I didn't. One of my other bosses died of lung cancer at 49 years old. He quit smoking and started exercising when they told him he had cancer. Too late. They cut out his vocal cords, then half his lung, then another half, and then some of his tongue, and then, it was over. I don't know if tobacco caused it, I'm not the doctor. I do know he smoked about three packs of non-filtered cigarettes a day. I also know when airlines prohibited smoking on planes, he started taking the train. I wished he had stopped sooner— he didn't want to, and he didn't think he could. Right up until they told him he was going to die, and then he found the will to quit. Don't wait for that kind of encouragement.

What I am having a hard time figuring out is why some of my friend's families haven't sued the restaurants whose food has caused the death of their loved ones. Think about this: If you smoke and get cancer, you sue the tobacco companies and get millions for you and the lawyers. Did anybody ever check to see if any of the plaintiffs' attorneys smoked? Wouldn't that be ironic? Sort of like a judge who is a functioning alcoholic, listening to a drunken driving case. Or a guy as fat as I was, telling employees not to do drugs. It's molasses calling the turtle slow. Anyway, what I have a problem understanding is how someone can eat several cheeseburgers a day, several orders of fries and pure sugar soda pop for years, have a massive heart attack, and not receive millions of dollars in compensation from the fast-food place that served them. Why haven't the fast-food places that serve high-cholesterol, salt-drenched, tons-of-fat, stomach-bursting, friendly dinners been sued by heart attack and stroke victims in a class-action suit? Maybe I missed something. To invite children to get a prize with every purchase, to have free drawings on each wrapper, to encourage more meals to be crammed down your throat, just so you, too, can soon collect all 400 pieces of a prize—but you have to hurry because this offer won't last forever, so come on in everybody, eat as much grease, fat, salt and sugar as humanly possible in the remaining time. Limited supply.

Think about this before you write me a letter. Write your mayor or congressman or whomever you think gives a damn. If cigarettes have to have warning labels on them, if car mirrors have to have warning labels on them, why doesn't the wrapper on the junk food have to say, "If you or your parents or your children eat very many of these, you will form horrible nutritional habits, greatly increasing your chance of a stroke or heart attack, and you will very probably look like a whale."

I don't know, maybe I'm getting a little cynical in my healthy old age. You know why there hasn't been a successful lawsuit? Because it's legal to stuff yourself with whatever kind of garbage you want to. It's legal, but that doesn't make it right.

Remember, this is the only place where you are both the doctor and the patient; poor food and addiction choices have consequences. The choice is yours. Stop eating whatever it is that's putting and keeping pounds of lard on your back, arms, hips, thighs, chins, all over your body. I had to stop doing the everyday ritual of devouring pancakes, syrup, "everything on a pig but the squeal," hash browns and toast breakfasts. I had to stop drinking myself into a six-figure income. Rule #3: STOP doing bad things to yourself.

#4 Start doing good things to yourself

This is the payoff. If you really want to get healthy, if you really make it a priority, if you do stop killing yourself, you must not stop there. There is one more thing to do.

The next step is equally important. Get in the game. Move that body. Get off the couch and on the bench (the weight bench). Use those muscles. Start doing good things to yourself. Take the money you were wasting on junk and buy good food. Take the money you spent being a big shot at the bars and get a gym membership. I like good clothes as much as the next fellow, but if the choice is a new shirt or vitamins, make it the vitamins.

Want to spend some money on yourself? Try a new pair of good gym shoes, a book on nutrition or a subscription to a health magazine. Go to a seminar on aging or cooking or something that will increase your knowledge of your health. You decide; it's your money. Again, you do not have to be a fanatic about this, but instead of doing all unimportant things, do some important things. I still buy a new blues album once in awhile. I love the blues, and I'm going to keep on listening to them. What I don't do is buy an album before I buy my groceries for the week. Start doing things that are improving your health and you won't be sorry.

I talked with a lady last night who did steps 1, 2 and 4. She just could not understand why she lost only a few pounds and was stuck. She doesn't understand this is "for life." You can't eliminate any of the rules and expect improvement. I cannot improve on Bill's book Body-*for*-LIFE. It works. Sometimes you might not be able to do exactly what the book suggests, but stay as close as you can. It works. This isn't a Body-*for*-LIFE book. At the beginning I said this is a "How in the hell did I get in such bad shape" book. I got in such bad shape by not wanting to change. I was comfortable in my misery. I was 260 pounds because I did not make my blood pressure a priority. I did bad things to myself on a steady basis, and more than anything else, I did nothing good for me but make money.

One more T-shirt memory. I once saw an enormous person wearing a T-shirt that had, "I have the body of a God" written on it. Upon closer examination, in very small letters it read, "Unfortunately, it's Buddha." Think about that for a minute. This obese person was advertising and making a joke on how unhealthy he was. He found some comfort in turning his unhealthy body into a joke.

Get the hell out of your misery, now! If you want a change, do it. If you don't want a change, don't waste your time.

—10—
The way I see it...
Being efficient isn't
the same as being effective

Two quick stories that make a lot of sense to me. There were three or four good ole boys from Georgia who loved to go fishing. They spent every free moment fishing. They would fish on their lunch hour if they were near water. They all owned the best rods and reels, they had the best tackle money could buy, the finest boat and state-of-the-art lures.

One of the fellows saw a fishing show that was broadcast from Canada, in the middle of the winter. A guy on the television was ice fishing and was standing there with a string of Northern Pike. That's all it took; the plans were made to take a trip to Canada.

They planned every day, and finally Christmas vacation came. Off they went to Canada. They arrived at the exact spot of the TV program. They unloaded the truck, bought live bait and ice picks at a nearby bait store. They were ready to get their fair share of the Great Northern Pike.

About an hour later, one of the three guys came back to the bait store and bought three more ice picks. An hour later he showed back up and got three more ice picks. Maybe two hours passed and he came back in and got five ice picks. A half-hour later he comes in and buys the last seven ice picks in the store.

Are you catching a lot of fish, the manager asks? "Not yet," replied the fisherman. "But we about got the hole big enough for the boat."

A guy living in California decides to take a vacation to Canada, but money is real tight and he has to plan out every detail. He wants to drive the back roads and really see America on his way. He gets out a map and plots his every move. He knows exactly how much to pack to eat; he knows exactly how much gas he will need. He has the car tuned up, and the tires have the precise amount of air. He won't use the air conditioner; that will lower his gas mileage. He sits in his living room night after night and plots and plans everything. He pulls the car up next to the house, packs it and leaves the next morning at exactly 6 a.m. He drives with all four windows down, and he will drive 450 miles at 55 miles per hour. Everything is perfect until he sees a sign that reads, "Welcome to Mexico!"

He had backed out of the driveway instead of pulling out forward. That then made turning to the right, a turn to the left. He was, of course, headed in the wrong direction. This is what we call being efficient, not effective.

I hope you remember these two little stories when you start your training. It won't much matter where you train, or what kind of equipment you use. It won't matter if you wear the latest fashion-approved workout attire. It just doesn't matter. If you are efficient, but not effective, you will not get the desired results.

We're back to the old deserted island theory. If you had no gym, no equipment, no trainer, or supplements, with very little food to be found and only the clothes on your back, you could still do sit-ups, push-ups, jog, shadow box and jumping jacks. You could do something and do it correctly.

When you walk in the place you train, be it your living room, the park, or the most exclusive private exercise room in town, you have to have a plan. What is your plan for today? Is it to do aerobics? Is it to train your upper body? Is it to work lower body? Did you work this particular muscle group yesterday or the day before? I do think the Body-*for*-LIFE Program is an excellent program to follow, but you must have some sort of plan, regardless of which program you follow. The guys fishing and the fellow going on vacation all had a plan. They knew where they wanted to go but were confused on what to do when they got there and which direction to turn.

Know your equipment. Both examples knew their boat and car. You need to know a few basic things about weights and gym equipment if you are going to use it. Most people don't use a "curling bar" to perform squats. Most people don't work the same muscles daily. Like me, you may have an injury or physical limitation that will prevent you from using a certain piece of equipment. You should know that before you start your program.

Going to a gym, a health club, or training at home is not advanced algebra. There are a few basic instructions you do need. There must be about a thousand books, videotapes and instructions out there that will give you a pretty good idea about exercise. Personal trainers, gym managers, coaches and friends who already train can help you. The local "Y" and most community centers have classes concerning health and exercise. I have trained in colleges (as a visitor, not a student) all over America that offer classes in beginning and advanced weightlifting. "I don't know how to work out with the weights" is not an acceptable excuse; it's like saying, "I don't know how to drive a car, and nobody will help me and there is no information to learn proper form." Not true!

Keep this on the low down, but I never touched a computer until I got to EAS. I'm telling you I could have flown a 747 easier than I could operate a personal computer. I had never needed one, and once my previous boss, Gene DuPont (a computer whiz), offered to give me one. I said, "No thank you, I don't need it." Truth was, I didn't know how to use it. The day I arrived at EAS they set up my office, then brought in a new computer and had it all set up for me. I spent two days looking for the on-off button. Finally, someone asked me why I hadn't answered their e-mail, and I said there was something wrong with my computer. A nice lady from the computer department came by and reported my PC worked just fine. After she turned it on, I was scared to turn it off, simply because I didn't know how to turn it back on.

I don't know if there is a computer heaven or not, but if there is, Ms. Linda Davis will be an angel up there. She was the most patient, kind and understanding lady I've ever learned from. She took me step by step through the basics and didn't make fun of me. She didn't laugh or embarrass me in any way. Trust me on this one, there are people in this world who will take you step by step and teach you the basics of working out with weights. Believe me, a computer is much, much more complicated. Just like the computer, you still have to do the work, but the reading, watching, listening and asking questions will make it much easier. Everybody around me was flying up and down his or her computer and I felt like I was in the Daytona 500 pushing a wheelbarrow. I was wrong—don't you be. Ask questions.

This brings me to three important rules I learned a long time ago. I was fortunate enough in my life to work with a police department for about two years. This was a long time ago, but I remember it quite clearly. I got hired on as a prison guard and served as courtroom security. When we didn't have prisoners, or were traveling with prisoners or sitting in court, I spent a little time in the squad room with the other deputies. I listened as these 20- and 30-year veterans talked about a lot of different things. Some told stories of law enforcement in the Deep South back in the '50s, '60s and '70s. They talked about cases they had worked and some they had solved. One deputy had been a military policeman for 25 years. He was one of the first "special-forces" veterans. He had pictures taken with President Kennedy at Ft. Bragg. All of that information will probably go into a book someday, if my mind stays clear. It was a long time ago. I hope I do remember it. Those were good men and women, who kept us safe for a long time.

A friend of mine worked there who had been a helicopter pilot in Vietnam, a policeman in Memphis and a Deputy U.S.

Marshal. He had seen a lot in his life, and he gave me some advice. I would like to share it with you. He said he had gotten it from an older policeman when he was younger, and it had worked well for him. Here it is… he said there were three rules for survival; always have been and always will be.

#1 Know your enemy
#2 Plan your escape
#3 Be familiar with your equipment

He was 100 percent right. You and I both know our enemy. We both know what kept us unhealthy for years. We know who at work is not trying to promote our ideas or us. And you will soon know exactly who doesn't want you to be healthy and better looking. Wait and see.

Plan your escape. Smarter words were never spoken. Why don't you have those words put on a plaque and set them on your desk or dashboard, where you can see them often. Want to get out of the rut you're in? Plan your escape. Got a monkey on your back; got a habit that's trying to control you? Plan your escape. In the dead-end, wrong job? Don't jump up and storm out the door; wait until it's convenient for you. Plan your escape.

Be familiar with your equipment. Go in the gym, walk into a health club, and visit a home-gym company. Touch the dumbbells, sit on the equipment; you don't have to sign up for a year. You don't have to buy anything. Look at the weights and become familiar with them. Let nothing intimidate you. They're just weights, and they're just there, waiting.

I have bought a used computer. I'm typing this book on it now. Thank God for the backspace key, but I'm getting better with each page. Let me take a minute and thank that policeman. His name was Joe Hendricks. I say "was" because he's gone. I really think if there's a need for a couple of policemen (maybe to direct chariot traffic) in eternity, the Lord will call on Joe Hendricks and Bob Parmenter. I was honored to know them, work with them and call them my friends. I want to take time to thank all those deputies. They were good, good men and women. They taught me a lot, and I stay in touch with most of them whenever possible.

Since I'm not writing a "how to" book, I don't know what equipment you will be using. It doesn't matter. You will know what you're going to use, so get familiar with it. Nobody born has the skill at birth to work on a computer or correctly perform resistance training. We all had to learn it. The greatest bodies had to walk in a gym the first time. They had to have a person, a dad or mom, or brother, sister, friend, someone, who showed them for the first time. I really do not believe anyone walked into a weight room and started doing perfect form and exact sequence rotation. It just doesn't happen. We all had to learn. The great bodybuilders and fitness enthusiasts had to start somewhere. They just started before you, and me, that's all.

Remember that the fisherman didn't need the boat. You may not need a three-year membership or a $100,000 home renovation for a gym. Likewise, don't back out of the driveway and make the wrong turn. Don't defeat yourself in the gym. Ask questions. Read books. Follow a good plan. To go to the gym and do the wrong exercise is better than doing nothing, but not much better. Time wasted is lost forever. I think that was Ben Franklin. I wonder if he lifted weights? He sure had the right idea about it.

—11—
The way I see it...
There's no shame in
reaching out for a helping hand

There are thousands of good men and women out there who spend their day ready and willing to save us. We don't know all their names, but when they crawl through broken glass or a burning building to save us, they become real important. There are men and women who do not know us, don't know our names, don't get invited to our house for dinner or drinks, and never get a birthday or holiday card from us, yet by dialing 911, they will respond, ready and willing to put their lives on the line for us as quickly as they can get there. Sure it's their job, sure they get paid for it, sure some days go by when they aren't called. Then there is the time they are called, and it's you who need them. How much do these people make, what is their salary? The only answer I can think of is... *how much is your life worth?*

Many years ago I went to work for a short time in two emergency rooms. You want to talk about a hell of a quick education? We might get to go all our lives without a trip to the emergency room, but if we do have to go, we have one objective: to get fixed or be there for someone we love to get fixed. And in a hurry. What I saw those ambulance drivers and the ER personnel do is amazing. There might be people working on you who you will never know. There might be someone who has their hand on your heart and you will never know their name or what steps they took to keep you or someone you love alive. I believe we not only owe these people a "thank you" when they save us, we owe them a "thank you" for being there just in case we do need them.

If in the future some bad people break into my house, shoot me and set all my furniture on fire, then steal my car and my television, I would like to take this opportunity to thank in advance everyone who shows up for work that day, responds to the call and has a hand in saving my life. They are the true heroes in my book. It sure couldn't be about the money. It couldn't be about having to work nights and weekends and what they have to deal with. It has to be like the solider who puts his or her life on the line for their country. It has to be about helping others; it's just got to be.

Can you imagine if you were in a wreck and the police, firemen and paramedics showed up and all of a sudden they said, "Oh goodness, look at the time, we're all off our shift in 10 minutes." Can you imagine a paramedic saying, "Gosh, you're right! It's nearly shift change and it's starting to drizzle, we're out of here. Sorry pal, but if you can get your car started, there's a hospital about two miles from here."

So you manage to drive to the ER, and you find the doors

locked. A guard inside yells through the glass doors, "Sorry, buddy, everybody goes home at 11. You might come back at 9 a.m. And would you mind not bleeding all over the sidewalk? Thanks. By the way, if you think you're going to die, there is an all-night gas station about three blocks down the street. Okay, thanks again, and good luck to you! Bye-bye now."

You're reading this saying that would never happen. You're right, it wouldn't. It's not just firemen and paramedics and police officers and ER personnel, it's also the power company linemen who go out on freezing nights when storms take our heat away. It's phone company workers who stay around the clock when a hurricane or disaster occurs. It's the men and women who get up at 3 a.m. and shovel snow off the highways so we can get where we're going during snowstorms.

Every lifeguard on the beach doesn't have styled hair with eight or 10 drop-dead gorgeous girls hanging around them. Plenty of lifeguards are alone with a lot of beach, pool or lake to watch and the responsibility for hundreds of people. They sit in the baking sun, keeping tabs on swimmers, surfers, fishermen and especially children. Often a thankless job. When we think about it there are a lot of jobs where the service performed is directly related to our comfort and safety. I'm sure you join me in thanking them from the bottom of our hearts.

That will bring me to one of the most important parts of my successful transformation. I'm speaking here for Porter, no one else. I'm speaking for Porter in this entire book. I can't speak for you or anyone other than myself. So here goes. I alone could not have done the transformation. Yes, I lifted the weights and yes, I turned down temptation. I did the aerobics, and I kept the fuse lit, but under no circumstances did I win anything by myself.

I was watching the Olympics and was aware of the people on the sidelines. The camera kept cutting over to the sideline to watch a coach, to interview a coach, or to get a coach's reaction. We often see this in boxing matches when an announcer goes into the fighter's corner and interviews the handler. We see it at every football game. The camera stays on the coach about half the time. What a wonderful word, "coach." It may not carry the weight the word "veteran" does, but in my book, it's more important than king or master or owner or boss. A coach teaches and trains and cares. If you're going to do this transformation, you have to do the work. Neither Bill Phillips, my dad, my employees, my boss, my roommate, my girlfriend, the gym owner or my coach did any of the work for me. You can't pay somebody to go exercise for you. You can't pay somebody to eat right for you. No more than you could pay somebody to go to church for you and think it was doing you any good in eternity. No one can do this for you. You can pay people to walk your dog, you can pay people to train for themselves, you can go buy a gym if you want to, but by now you know that you and you alone have to do the work to get healthy.

We know there are plenty of folks who will help you survive; you still have to have the will to live. Same thing with this transformation—you have to sweat. You can train alone; you can go buy a set of weights and put them in your house and use them all by yourself with great results. Several Body-*for*-LIFE Champions did just exactly that. So we know it doesn't matter where you train as long as you stick to it. What else do we know? A) There are people who will help you. B) You have to do the work. C) Nobody does this completely alone. That's what I want to tell you, the truth. I didn't do it alone.

Back in 1997 it was a matter of a few weeks when all the people I knew fell into two distinct categories. They were either with me or against me. No gray area. I hardly told anybody I was doing this Challenge. It wasn't their business, and I didn't want to admit how bad of shape I was in. I did tell my coach, Eric Shrieves. I could probably write three books on our 25-year friendship, but nobody would believe it. Let me say this, when I walked into the Steel Mill gym, I looked like a raisin in a peach pie. A 260-pound human whale… I felt real out of place. Eric was the manager, and I walked up to the desk, showed Eric the article in *Muscle Media* magazine and said I wanted to do this. He looked at the article, closed the magazine, threw it up on the desk and said the three most important words of the entire 12 weeks: *"Let's do it."* If he had said, "Hell no, Porter, you will re-injure your shoulder, and you can't lose that much weight in 12 weeks, don't waste your time with this," I wouldn't have done it. He said, "Let's do it." Well, you know the results; in 14 weeks I got rid of 74 pounds of fat and put on 10 pounds of muscle. He told me I should drop 20 pounds and then go in the Challenge at 240. It took me exactly two weeks to get to 240 pounds. I started exercising, and I quit drinking two six packs a day. "LET'S DO IT!"

I also went to my boss, Gene DuPont. I asked him if I could take my lunch at different times and if I could jockey my schedule to get my workouts in. He said, "I know you will get your work done, do whatever you need to do." He knew I would never ever neglect my job, and I never did.

Thank you, Gene, you are one of the best men a person could know. I'm honored to call you my friend. Then there was my roommate, Jim McCain. He played as important a part in this as anyone. He moved the parties next door. He saw to it, when it was obvious that I was hell-bent for leather on doing my best, that his friends kept the noise down to a "low roar." He went on living and enjoying a pizza and a cold beer, but he was always very considerate of what I was doing.

I certainly had the desire to change. I had the determination and unyielding focus to stay on course. You have it also—you simply have to tap into it and use it. I had reinforcements from my friends who helped me. My enemies didn't care why I was losing weight and certainly didn't understand why I wasn't drinking anymore. They weren't personal enemies, they were "goal enemies." It wasn't that they wanted me to fail; it was that their agenda had consequences that created failure. How's that?

This success can only be achieved by you. But it's so helpful to have the love and support of people around you who want you to succeed. It might be hard for you to believe, but in some situations there are people who will NOT want you to succeed. I know that sounds crazy, but it's true, true, true. I don't know if miserable people want company or if insecure people don't want anyone to improve; I just don't know. I do know and did experience seemingly innocent people trying to sabotage my progress. "Come on and have a drink." "Is that all you're going to eat?" "We're going to order pizza, do you want some?" and on and on.

Try cutting out the fattening things in your normal life and see how difficult it is. Innocent birthday parties at the office offer you about 50 grams of fat and untold calories and carbohydrates. And it's innocent. Girls were always bringing in cookies and cake and ordering out, and there was food, beer and soda everywhere. When you finally get tired of saying, "No thank you" to all the bad things to eat, you ought to consider saying, "No thank you" to the people who keep on trying to get you to cheat. Watch some people get mad because you won't have that piece of pie or drink with them. Watch some of your friends gather behind your back and gossip about how you're losing weight. See if they don't tell you, "Now don't lose too much weight, you don't want to get sick." Didn't they see how sick you were at 30 pounds overweight? I promise you some people will say you're just not yourself anymore. Damn right you're not yourself anymore—you're the new, healthy you!

I can't tell you how many times Eric called me and asked, "What did you eat, how do you feel, did you take your supplements, are you sleeping okay?" He didn't just write my schedules and then never speak to me again; he was honestly concerned about how I was doing. When I would stagger in the gym at 2:30 a.m. for a workout (not drunk, just tired), Eric was there in spirit. He didn't show up and train with me, but his heart and words and encouragement were there for every rep. He has always been there. I hope you have a friend like Eric, it helps. I hope my words and concern are with you when it seems like you can't go on. You *can* go on, and I really care if you do. Why? Because somebody cared if I made it, and that levels out a few rough spots in the road. Thank you, Eric.

Sometimes it seems a person may be hurting you when they're trying to get the best work out of you. I hated going to the doctor when I was a little boy. He stuck me with a mean old needle. I didn't realize he was trying to help me; I just knew it hurt. I didn't like one of my PE teachers. He made me run around the track, and I wanted to sit on my butt in study hall. I wish now he had made me run all day. I had a martial arts instructor who made me try to punch the sun from coming up. It came up, and I had to do push-ups for 20 minutes. Maybe someday that exercise will save my life. Did you have a drill instructor who you hated? Was he or she trying to teach you how to stay alive? Everybody who is hard on you isn't trying to hurt you; not always. Sometimes they are, and I don't know how to tell you how to tell the difference. Eric might push you, but he won't hurt you.

Remember, when the gold medalists cross the finish line, they're not alone. Their parents, teachers, loved ones and coaches are crossing the line with them. It's sort of sad and wonderful at the same time. The athlete gets the glory and the attention and the big offers and that's how it should be. But, somewhere in the crowd, a coach smiles and fades away behind a rush of journalists and photographers. The coach's reward is your victory. Sure they get paid, but one more time, it ain't never been about money. It has to be about pride and love and character for a coach.

You mark this down in your book. I'm not good enough to compete in the Olympics in the Senior Men's Checker Division.

I don't think I've ever been vain or a big shot or anything like that. People who know me think the same thing. I'm not a loud mouth or a show off. But on the one chance in 10 million that I had ever been good enough to compete in the Olympics, suppose I had won. I swear I would have given the medal to my parents and my coach and my friends. I would have gone and sat down and let them run the victory lap. That night Bill gave me the jacket and ring (along with nine other wonderful champions), I didn't win it—it belonged to Eric and Gene and Jim and the Steel Mill Gym. I was just the guy they sent to collect it. Thank you guys, all of you are the Champion.

This isn't a 1970's crime movie; you don't need to keep your enemies close to you. Keep your real friends close to you these 12 weeks. Enter the Challenge, or don't, but change your unhealthy body into a healthy body. Remember me, or don't, but know I want you to succeed. I want you to feel as good about yourself as I know you can. I'm not going to tell you it's easy. I am going to tell you it's the easiest hard thing you can do. It's hard, but once you make your mind up and decide to get back in control, it gets real easy. Get some help. Turn to *your* Eric. Find your best friend and ask him or her to help you. If you are a very, very fortunate person, your friend will look up at you and say, *"Let's do it!"*

—12—
The way I see it…
We wind up paying a high price
for low-nutrient "value meals"

The flight I was on has just landed. Thank you, American. Everyone did his or her part, and I'm safe to fly again. My part was to weigh the same as I did when I boarded the plane this morning. And I do. At the airport I had a delicious turkey sandwich, minus the bread and mayo, a crisp red apple and a cup of coffee. Of course, I had water throughout the day. I will eat again today, and I will eat tonight. I won't be hungry. What else I won't be is carrying around a ton of empty calories and fat and carbohydrates and sugar. I used to, but not anymore.

What did you eat this morning? How many meals have you had today? How much of the fuel you took in have you burned off? What kind of fuel did you put in your motor today? Was it high octane or regular? Did it burn clean or were there lots of particles left to float around in your system? Did you eat anything at all?

I swear I know people who wash and wax their car on a set

schedule. They polish the dashboard and ask people to dust their shoes off before they get in. The tires are shined, and you could see the reflection of your teeth in the wheels. They change the oil at exactly 3,000 miles and wouldn't think of putting anything in the tank except top-grade, super-premium gasoline. After they dry and polish the car, they stand back and knock off a can of soda pop or a couple of cans of beer. Then they drive the car to a favorite drive-in restaurant, have a double-cheeseburger bomb, and stand around admiring other cars and smoke a half pack of cigarettes. They make plans to go to the local bar that night and see more beautiful cars and repeat the entire process all over again. I should know. I did it for years. Now that I look back, I don't understand why I loved my car so much and took such good care of it, yet abused myself. Know anybody like that? It was a 1970 Chevrolet SS Monte Carlo, black body, black top, and black leather interior. That car was probably still running strong on February 12, 1997, when I couldn't even run to the corner!

What did you do this morning to the most important vehicle you will ever own, your body? Did you wash it? Did you take a toothbrush and shine it? Did you take deodorant or cologne and make it smell good? Did you put clean clothes on it and then sit down and load it with junk or fattening fuel? Think about that for a minute. Why would you, and why did I, clean, polish and dress up our bodies and then make a conscious effort to fill them up with garbage? I don't have the answer. I simply know that not filling up with garbage is soooo much more intelligent and far healthier than the alternative.

Would you put used motor oil in your car? Would you run low-octane gas in your car? Would you constantly put used worn-out hoses and bald tires on the car? If saving money is the reason, then I assure you it costs a lot less for egg whites and oatmeal than it does to have donuts, toast and jelly, a fruit turnover with icing, and a bowl of high-sugared cereal with whole milk. Not all breakfast food is bad for you. It's up to you to read labels and then, like your car, make an intelligent decision!

How did I get to 260 pounds? I ate my way there. I would get up, go to a favorite "breakfast" place and get the special. It was special all right; they should rename it the heart clogger. Maybe they could call it the ER special. And I loved it. I ordered it every time and it tasted good every time. I never thought once about what I was eating, and besides, everybody else was eating the same thing. I remember thinking how happy I was I could get that breakfast special 24 hours a day, every day. Boy oh boy, I could clog my arteries any time of the day or night. The wait staff was always happy to see me coming; I tipped a lot, and I always cleaned my plate. I wonder if they miss me? Probably not. I'm sure someone else has taken my place.

If I haven't lost you, if you are still reading this, stay with me. There's a real important point coming up. Let's see if I can make sense. We're told and taught from childhood to eat a big breakfast. My great-grandparents got up every morning and cooked for eight or 10 people. They were farmers and went out six days a week and worked the land. My great-grandmother taught my grandmother how to cook, and my grandmother passed those lessons down to my mother, who 45 years ago made me a big breakfast to start the first grade. Wrong, wrong, wrong.

Unless you are going to get up tomorrow at about 4 a.m., start a wood fire in the stove, go out and hitch up a team of mules, and plow 40 acres of hard-bottom land in south Georgia, why in the hell would you need a 300-grams-of-carbohydrate, 200-grams-of-fat, 3,000-calorie six-biscuit breakfast? I don't, you don't, and unless you're plowing or training to be a Sumo wrestler, nobody does. We're not our grandparents, and we don't need to eat like them. Of course, your job affects how you should eat, just as your lifestyle dictates how much fuel you need and when you need it. If you sit behind a computer all day, you won't need as much fuel as a person loading furniture. Common sense.

Let me stop right here and be real honest with you. I barely got out of high school. It took me 14 years to pass 12 grades. I'm not educated in any college, trade school, vocational school or correspondence course. I walked across that stage 35 years ago, went back to my seat, took off my cap and gown, placed them on top of my diploma in the chair I'd been sitting in and walked out the door of the Bell Auditorium in Augusta, Georgia. As far as I know, unless the janitor got them, they're still sitting there. I tried college a couple of years later and that was a bigger disaster than high school. My education came from life's experiences. It came from making mistakes and not listening to people smarter than me. I went with the crowd, and making a few dollars was more important than school. I never did everything I wanted to do, but I did damn little of what I didn't want to do. I wasted a lot of years, and I was unhealthy a lot of years both mentally and physically. I never got into trouble, I didn't do anything *really* wrong, I just wasted all my time. Until, one day, in one minute, I made the U-turn that you, too, can make. I started on the road of undoing as much damage as possible, in the time allowed. You can do it, too. Get off Regret Street and get on Recovery Road.

I'm not going to debate correct amounts of fats, carbohydrates, sugar, calories or protein with anybody. I can't say to do this exercise program or follow that nutritional program or even which supplement is best. I have taken only one nutritional supplement brand and it is EAS. How could I say if another brand is good or not? I can't. I could no more voice an opinion on other supplements or programs than I could write an article on the advantages of owning a Rolls Royce. I've never owned one.

I do know what I was eating, what I was drinking, what I wasn't doing and what I was doing that got me to 260 pounds at 30 percent bodyfat. That's almost 80 pounds of pure, useless, heart-clogging fat. I got down to 186 pounds at about 12 percent bodyfat and have stayed under 200 pounds for over seven years. I guess that gives me a Ph.D. in control! That's the main thing I can fall back on to give me the authority to write this book; *I did it*. You can do it, too. You can. In 1997, the year I won my category in the EAS Physique Transformation Challenge, nine other Champions also won with me. Some put on muscle, some took off fat, and they all turned their lives around. They are true Champions. Some of them had advanced degrees; some (like me) had high school educations. This ain't about degrees. It's not about a master's degree or bachelor's degree or a GED. It's not about being a Private or a Captain or a Colonel or an Admiral. I admire and respect education and wish I could go back and get one. That isn't what this is about. Do you know some educated fools? How somebody could sit through four, six, or more years of school and be that smart and at the same time let themselves go physically is beyond me. I know smart people who I trust with important issues who smoke two packs of cigarettes a day. I don't get it.

We've had doctors, lawyers, judges and blue-collar men and women accept the same Challenge I took. They all accepted it equally. And they've succeeded or failed equally. This is not about money or position or rank. The blanket of poor choices and poor health and lack of control covers everyone equally. Making the choice to buy a bottle of liquor, a pack of smokes or a half-pound of fried fatty meat with french fries and a 75-grams-of-sugar milk shake isn't measured by one's I.Q. Bad choices are made by smart people and not-so-smart people alike. I know another truth: that there's at least a fitness I.Q. upgrade when you choose to change your poor habits and become healthy.

—13—
The way I see it…
Nothing tastes as
good as being fit feels

It's a Saturday morning, and I'm off today. I've got 24 hours to myself to do exactly what I want. Right now I'm doing my laundry. I hate doing laundry. Here I sit in this Laundromat, watching my clothes spin round 'n' round. Don't get me wrong. I love being clean, and I really like fresh, clean clothes. But, I really *hate* doing laundry! Pretty soon I will be clipping coupons and exchanging recipes with the other Laundromat regulars.

Coming here is a lot like going to the gym and working out. I don't much like that either, but I *love* the results. Fact is, this whole transformation experience is a lot like doing laundry. We come here with dirty clothes. We put our choice of detergent in the machine and let it go to work. In about an hour the clothes are clean and dry and we take them home and iron them, hang them up and then wear them when we need to.

What's the difference between that and us taking an unhealthy body to the gym for about an hour workout, using the right supplements and nutrition, taking our body to the shower, rinsing it off and wearing it again? Not much, as far as I'm concerned.

That might seem silly, but it's not. You wouldn't wear dirty clothes over and over, would you? So why in the world would you wear an unhealthy body over and over?

Maybe because it's "socially acceptable" to be rail thin or fat but *not* socially acceptable to stink. There isn't a fashion designer alive who can cut a piece of cloth to hide odor. But we can all (including me) figure out ways to dress and hide our unhealthy bodies.

People are very inventive when they need to be. I was real quick to accept any invitation to a social event that called for a tux or a suit or business attire. What I found excuses for was pool parties, fishing trips (in the summer) and pick-up basketball games (shirts and skins). Things weren't always that way; they slowly evolved. You can't live in Florida for 20 years and not go to the beach. I'd even lived at the beach. I'd been in pretty good shape a long time ago. It was the last six or seven years before my 84-day transformation that I had absolutely gone to hell.

The more I ate and drank, the more excuses I found, and the further and further the beach and pool slipped away. That's funny... the Atlantic Ocean was in my backyard, but as far as me using it, it might as well have been on the other side of the world.

Where are you? How far away is the pool from you right this minute? I'm never going to look like Mr. America or any of the fabulous bodies I see in some of the muscle magazines. It just ain't gonna happen. What *will* happen to you and me is we're not going to be held hostage to a life indoors during the summer because we're ashamed or embarrassed to take our shirts off. No way ever again.

Let's you and me declare war on lost summers. You, too, can make the transformation I've made, and then we'll be free together. Picture it like this: Every time you put another forkful of junk or empty calories in your mouth, you are strengthening the chain that binds you to misery. *Don't do it.* This is simple—healthy food and exercise begins to dissolve the chain that binds us to misery. Eating unhealthy food and drink while sitting on the couch increases the strength of those chains.

It's the same with clothes. If they get dirty, we wash them in detergent and then they become clean again. As we wear them they get dirty. We have to clean them again, then the cycle continues. Why did I wear a dirty body for so long, then hide it under clean clothes? Because it was the easy way to exist; not live mind you, but exist. Is that what you're doing? Thank God, and a few people, that in 1997 I made the decision to let my body catch up with my clean clothes. What you will do is not my choice, it's not the mayor's choice and it's not your husband's or wife's choice. It's not the governor's choice or anybody else's choice. The rock-bottom choice is *yours* and yours alone.

Are you going broke because you spend all your money on cigarettes? Quit! Are you looking at a year in jail because you got your second DUI? Quit drinking and driving! Are you skin and bones because you think you're too fat? Eat something good for you! What job in this world is more important than your health? What person in this world is worth your health? Are you ridiculously fat because those cookies ran down the aisle, then jumped into your shopping cart and rode home with you? Did they hide in the cabinet, and when you went to bed and were sleeping did they scurry out of the bag, sneak down the hall, and while you were sound asleep, climb up the covers and one at a time jump into your mouth (between your teeth) to commit suicide? Horseshit! You're doing it yourself. I was doing it to myself, we both need to QUIT! Clean clothes, clean body, clean life. We can do it!

—Part Three—
Staying the Course

—14—
The way I see it…
You've gotta want to change as much in hour two, day three and week four as you do right this second

Every July 4, we as a nation head to the city park to watch fireworks light up the evening sky. As the rockets are lit and propelled toward the stars, the fuse burns till it reaches its end when suddenly the park is aglow with sparkles, sounds and beautiful colors. When one of the rockets really explodes and the sky catches fire, the crowd "ooohs" and "ahhhhs."

What's the one thing that must happen for this celebration to occur? Simple, the fuse has to stay lit. There it is in a nutshell. You must maintain and retain the fuse that right this second is being lit. When you say, "I want to do this transformation," you have "lit the fuse," neighbor.

If you keep that fuse lit, in about 84 days, you will be running around in a dazzling, new firecracker of a body. People will be "ooohing" and "ahhhing" over the new you.

Every Champion I've ever spoken with (including myself) has said the same thing. They used different terms, and said it in a different way. They may have been a Champion in a different sport, but they told me, and I'm telling you, *they kept the fuse lit until the explosion!*

I think that's it. I think we just cracked the safe. The deep, dark, chained-up secret to control and success has just been exposed. *You must want a transformation as much in hour two, day three and week four as you do right this second.*

People don't stop, fail or quit before they start—that's impossible. You can't quit something you've never done. People either don't do this, or they start then finish at some level or degree. To finish successfully you must keep the fuse lit. Real simple. Why do people stop? They stop because the fuse has fizzled out. People tell me they stop because it becomes too difficult. No, hell no it doesn't! It doesn't, it doesn't, it doesn't. They say they quit because the journey is too hard. Listen closely, the journey is the reward, the fuse is the journey and the result is the explosion. It's beyond me how anyone can sit through four years of college, graduate, and then not be able to execute 84 days toward a lifetime of good health. You should hear some of the conversations between me and people with advanced degrees.

Please, I'm begging, light the fuse within you and keep it lit. There's no greater pain than what could have been. Try this: "When the end arrives, sorrow and regret are far greater when challenges have gone unmet."

We can all do this transformation thing. We could put anyone on a island out in the ocean, feed them exactly what they should eat, make them do exactly the right exercises, drink the exact amount of water and in 12 weeks they would be in great shape. Kinda like boot camp. What happens there is 100 percent control. The results would be a 100 percent improved body, but there may be no change in the mind. Of course this island and boot camp society isn't going to happen. They haven't passed a law yet saying being unhealthy is against the law. So we will continue to have to drive past five or six fast-food or donut parlors to get to a gym.

I will never forget, on the way to the gym in Orlando, I had to drive by an ice-cream place everyday. It got to the point that I would stop on that corner only long enough to check traffic and then proceed. Then I got to the point that I wouldn't look at the building. Then I tried to go by the ice-cream place only after it was closed. It usually was at 2:30 a.m. The days I trained during the day, I would refuse to look at it. Guess what? Now I don't care if they open one next door to me—I won't go in it just because it's there. I kept the fuse lit!

You can do it; I didn't do anything except want to be healthy as much on day 84 as I did on day one. Sometimes I see life like a pinball. We come roaring out of the shoot and start moving all over the board. Along the way, we score some points and sometimes we foul out. We get a second chance and sometimes a third and fourth. We head toward the bottom of the table and sometimes a flipper sends us back in the game. We might score some more points, and bells and lights go off and we get rewards and credits. Sometimes we don't get any points. Sooner or later we slip past the flippers and go in the hole at the bottom. Our points are added up and our score is posted. Someone else comes behind us and tries their best to beat our score. The one big difference in a pinball and us is this: Gravity is constantly pulling the pinball down, but we pull ourselves down. Although the end result is the same, the quality of the game is a direct result of the choices, commitment and amount of attention we've paid.

Pay attention to your health, keep the fuse lit, want it and make it a priority. The game will end; score as many points and stay in the game as long as you can. We're talking about your body and mind here. The healthier you are, the more lights, bells and whistles you're gonna get in this game of life. Keep the fuse lit!

—15—
The way I see it…
If you can't go with someone
as good as you, go alone

Positive influence may not always work, but negative influence *always* works. Let me remind you I'm talking from experience. There are thousands of names in the yellow pages of social workers and therapists and doctors, all educated people, who can better explain and correct life's little "get me downs." One time I thought I was really cracking up. Something real bad had happened to me, and I swear I didn't know if I was coming or going. Worse than that, I didn't care. I was going to do something stupid to myself, and I came real close. This isn't true confession time; I just want you to know I've been there. I was at the end of the trail and thought getting off was the only step left.

In an earlier chapter, I said there was no such thing as almost dead or a little bit pregnant. No gray area. In the bar business we say, "It ain't late 'til 2, and then it's too late." The bars in Florida close at 2 a.m. I was almost at 2 a.m., but not quite. The punch line here is I had to find some relief somewhere, somehow. I really didn't want to face another day in such painful internal grief. I'm not talking about the loss of a family member or a fire taking my home. Those are real problems and deserve a time of remorse and sincere grieving. What I'm talking about is letting negative people who say negative things and do negative things, get to us. Never again! I will never again invite other people's "crap" into my life. Don't you let them into your life, either.

I had let it happen. I had invited it. I thought I was pretty sharp, but nobody is so slick they're not due for one more greasing! This was the second stupidest thing I ever did. The first was to associate with the wrong people.

Finally, I called my family doctor. He was listed in the yellow pages with all the other helpful people. I'm thankful to this day that I called him. I don't think I would be here writing this if I hadn't. Remember that I was one step from getting off the trail. Have you been there? Are you there now? I look back and see how stupid I was, but at the time, this was the real McCoy.

My doctor made me an appointment and told me to come on in. I got there, went in an examining room, sat down and waited. He came in, started to ask how I was and didn't get one full sentence out before I started crying my eyes out. After I cried my eyes out, I cried my heart out. Then I cried my stomach out. There were tears, sweat, mucus, spit; I did everything in that chair except number two. He sat there looking at me. A nurse walked in, and I had no idea he could move that fast but, he snapped his fingers, pointed at the door and she was out of there like he had diagnosed me with leprosy.

After about 30 minutes of this uncontrolled sobbing, I caught my breath and sort of chuckled. Somewhere in the back of my mind I could hear Joe Cocker singing, "Cry me a river, I cried a river over you." Then I laughed a little, and then I laughed a lot, then had a good, long, deep, out-loud laugh. He sat there stone-faced looking at me. Finally the laughing went away and the room was completely silent. It was over. He sat on the examination table with his legs swinging over the side, and I had not moved out of the chair the entire time. I got up and with God as my witness said, "Do you think I need professional help?" With out blinking an eye, he said, "No, you'll be all right now."

I said thank you, wiped my eyes and walked out of the room, down the hall and out of his office. Nobody in the office or behind the desk said one word to me. Whether they knew it or not, they had witnessed an exorcism. I had made a *conscious decision* that day, that hour, to get the negative people out of my life, or else end it.

A couple of weeks later I got a bill from him for $125. That's $25 a word. Remember, I started my crackup before he could say hello, how are you, how's the weather or anything. He said five words, "No, you'll be alright now." Let me save you $125 or whatever it costs these days.

Here goes... my grandmother said, "Porter, if you can't go with someone as good as you, go alone." Here are some more: "Water seeks its own level." Here's another, "Birds of a feather flock together." Try this one: "Be ye not unequally yoked."

Listen, if you are being held down or held back by another person, you're making that choice. I once wrote that if someone you are involved with was pulling you in the gutter, find out how much that person weighs because that's exactly how much weight you need to lose immediately!

Jealousy and spite don't care about age, race, sex, religion— nothing. If someone in your home or workplace doesn't want you to get better, you probably won't. Not only do you have to fight your own demons, but you also have to fight theirs. I'm not saying it can't be done; I'm saying it's very helpful to have a goal, a commitment and a positive support team. I'm not telling you to leave an unhappy home in order to have a great body and to get fit. I am telling you to make the decision to improve your health, and then you will find out quickly who does and who doesn't want you to improve. You will find a silver thread running through this little book about keeping bad influences (especially people) out of your way.

I did a quick inventory of all of my "friends" when I started the transformation. The ones who didn't want me to succeed got transferred out of my program. Not out of my life, they were still my friends. They were just not going to ambush my getting healthy. I didn't have another $125 to give the doctor. Some friends are worth dying for; no friend is worth keeping who wants you to be unhealthy. Do you honestly think the drug pusher wants you to clean up? Hell no. Do you think the liquor store is going to pay for your rehab? What makes you think that people who are trying to feed you unhealthy food with the sole purpose of keeping you fat, want you to be healthy? Think about it. Some of my friends tried hard to get me to have a drink in those 84 days. You are going to be amazed at who tries to sabotage you when you start improving.

—16—
The way I see it…
Don't try to teach a pig to sing; it wastes your time and annoys the pig

I don't argue with nobody about nothing. This is America, and you and I are entitled to our opinions about everything. That includes this book. When folks ask me about my workouts or nutrition plan, I'm glad to answer them truthfully. When they start disagreeing with me and correcting my routine, the conversation is over. You will find there are some people who do not want you to get fit. Isn't that crazy? I could never understand that, but I watched it happen and have read about it happening over and over again in the Body-*for*-LIFE Challenge competition packets we receive. If a pig wants to wallow in the mud and wants some company, you don't have to go. You will hear things like, "That's not healthy," and, "Why don't you act your age?" You may hear, "Are you trying to be a show off?" "Are you too good to have a drink with me?" Or my favorite, "Oh come on, have a little bite, it won't hurt you." *Oh, hell yes it will.*

Find what works for you, and do it. If hanging upside-down

from a clothesline and beating yourself with a Virginia ham works for you, then do it. I don't think it will, but who am I or anyone else to tell you it won't work? We don't know. Try hanging from the clothesline and beating yourself with a ham. If in 12 weeks you've lost about 50 percent of your fat and put on five or six pounds of muscle, if your heart rate is in a healthy range, if you are a new person, then count me in on the "clothesline and ham" routine. Again, I don't think at this point it will work, but it might. Remember to "fail fast" so you don't waste time. I do know there are some programs out there that have a great, proven track record, but I do not, nor does anyone else, know all of them.

Please listen to me! The clothesline approach is as silly as trying to change people's minds who absolutely do not want you to get healthy and do not want to get healthy themselves. Do not waste your time. Do not waste their time. And like politics and religion, do not waste your time arguing about it. I'm as guilty about this as anyone. I'm a Baptist. Nothing is going to change my mind or denomination. I'm going to stay a Baptist. That's that. End of subject. I'm sure there is a religion, person, political party, cause or something that all the "king's horses" couldn't make you change your mind about. Good, 'cause you've got to believe in something. If you don't think resistance and weight training and proper nutrition is the answer to a much healthier life, don't do it. Please write me when you find the magic pill, or when you get the pig to sing, whichever comes first.

—17—
The way I see it…
Insecurity and hate go hand in hand;
quit holding hands with either of them

It's December 7th. I'm fortunate enough to be in Honolulu today. It isn't Sunday; it's a Thursday. Nonetheless, it's a sad, sad day. I'm not hung up on this Pearl Harbor theme; I'm just amazed at how unfortunate it is to hate one another. There's no question that at some point in your life it may be necessary to take a stand and protect yourself or someone you love. It goes without saying there are some evil people in this world with bad intentions. But to slaughter thousands of people because a king, emperor or an elected official declares it should be is beyond me. If you really want to experience sad, come to Pearl Harbor.

This morning I watched the news and listened to a Pearl Harbor survivor state that he didn't hate the enemy pilots, they were just doing what they were told to do. He hated the leaders of the enemy country for causing such unnecessary human destruction.

I need to try and tie this in with getting healthy. So, I think hate and insecurity are powerful motivators. They are both destructive emotions, and for the life of me, I can't think of any productive results from either one. All things being equal, if you get in great physical shape and begin living a healthy lifestyle, a lot of insecurity goes out the window. There's something about making those little gains in the gym and on the scale that gives you more and more confidence and less insecurity.

Like whenever you make that first 20-minute aerobic workout, it might not feel good while you're doing it, but it sure feels good when you're done. Believe me, I would like to win the lottery and have a million dollars. But I think it would be just as good to work and write and earn a million dollars, maybe feel even a little better. I hope I find out either way and hope you do, too!

Would it be fair to say some insecurity evaporates with each new achievement? I think so. You try to do something new or something that is a little different, give it your best effort, and then when you succeed, it feels good. You can have these little doses of positive affirmation each day you stay on course, eating and living healthy. It's kinda like how you felt when you made an A+ in school. Each day that you live and eat healthy, give yourself a good grade. When you screw up, you get an F. Maybe "cheat meals" should be Bs; the whole day of "cheating" should be a C day. You figure it out.

When we have to drink booze and eat junk all day, or use drugs and steal from work, then there are some real deep issues of insecurity going on. Stop feeding them. If the insults and bad experiences are coming from another living human being, then refuse them from this day forward. Then the only direction you will be going in when you stop the insecurities will be forward. More accomplishment, less insecurity, more control, less fear. I promise you, when the fear and insecurities disappear, the hate goes with it.

Please don't confuse this with a total dislike for something or someone that has or is trying to hurt you. I'm talking about *do not fear* going into the gym because you think some in-shape bodybuilder will laugh at you. Do not think you will fail before you ever try. Do not let other people who may have a little temporary control of your life cause you to go the rest of your life thinking that you're worth less than you really are. There's only one of you, and you should take it to its full potential. Don't wait another day.

Wonder why we hate, and when we do, why do we hang onto it? It breeds nothing but decay. You can bet the farm on this one, I have damn sure hated some people in my life. I was wrong. You are worth exactly what you think you are worth. And I think you are priceless. You have the right to like or dislike whatever you want. You don't have to like every person you come in contact with. All those men at the bottom of Pearl Harbor, and thousands of men and women like them, paid for that privilege. So the question comes up, do we have the right to hate one another? I think we certainly do. Have at it; let it consume you if you wish. I've got other more important things to do. I finally realized it was a total waste of my time, and it changed nothing.

I also find that insecure people enjoy pointing out contradictions. Someone will write me and ask if I love Ted

Bundy. How ridiculous! I don't love Ted Bundy or anyone like him. But I'm not going to use him as an excuse to go get drunk or eat a key-lime pie. I won't use the stock market as an excuse not to work out. I also won't use Ted Bundy to start a war with anyone who happened to know him.

A landlord cheated me out of some money once. I was young and not the sharpest tool in the shed, and I lost my two-month's deposit. Boy was I mad. Anything like that ever happen to you? There was just nothing I could do about it—just nothing. I have two choices: I can let it go, or hold on to it and let it eat me up, day after day, the rest of my life. What are you holding onto that would be better off gone from your life? Don't waste time on something that isn't coming back or not getting done. Someone very dear to me was assaulted once. She survived with a few cuts and bruises, lost her pocketbook, and was scared into hysterics. Now I've got to tell you, I wanted to find that guy and do my dead-level best to beat the ever-loving dog $#&* out of him. I don't know who he was and probably never will, but I would like to. I can hate that it happened, I can hope it never happens again, I can pray he found some sort of religion and took up another line of work besides mugging single women in parking lots. What I can't do is let that horrible experience that happened to someone I loved prevent anything good from ever coming into my life.

Let go of any unnecessary hate or jealously that you have been holding on to. Redirect that energy and effort into something positive and productive. We can spend all our time and money hating cancer or we can spend all our time and money trying to cure it. The choice is ours.

Have you ever had a sweetheart who left you? I sure have; more than once. I hated both of them for a long time. You could say I sort of held onto that pain. Why? Was I insane? Evidently. What in the hell was I thinking about? She was gone, he was happy, and I was alone. Now, what would make me feel better? Okay, I know, I ate enough food to keep a company of Airborne Rangers marching for a week, and I drank myself into oblivion. I gained about 30 pounds in a few months and made myself more unattractive than I was. Of course, I was miserable, less attractive to the opposite sex and spending all my money on junk to make me feel better. I hated everybody. What an idiot I was.

Listen, if you think your sweetie is fixing to leave you, and you don't want them to go, don't take the low road. Don't run out and start making yourself more unattractive. If anything, start taking care of yourself. Drop a few pounds, tighten up a few loose ends, and try making yourself more appealing. The worst thing that can happen is your sweetie goes on and leaves you anyway and now you're better looking and ready to find a new one. Don't work hard at hating them, yourself, and everyone around you.

Do not for one minute think that no one else will want you; someone will! Do not think if you are the one leaving that nobody wants the person you're leaving behind. Someone will. The key is to not sit on the couch when you are alone and pine away. If you see the end coming and there's nothing you can do about it, get yourself in motion; don't waste time hating other people and yourself. Improve what is now available, for someone else to love.

One more time: I understand hate and hurt and insecurity.

133

I have wallowed in all three of them. If your boss, partner or a friend asks you to do something dishonest, don't do it. They are willing to sacrifice you to further their cause. What if all those enemy pilots on December 7th had stood up and said NO! What did Pearl Harbor accomplish? That is the saddest place I've ever been in my life.

Try not to be insecure; nothing good comes from that either. If I had to have a "pose down" against Arnold Schwarzenegger on stage, I wouldn't feel insecure; I would feel like a damn fool! It would be the same thing as trying to box Evander Holyfield. I wouldn't feel insecure, and I would eventually feel the clean, crisp sheets in the hospital when I woke up. I mean, know your limits, but do not be insecure about growing or improving. Compete at your level or a little above. You will continue to improve. If you want to hate something or feel insecure about something, then pick a wasted life to hate. Find a life that has been thrown away that could have been so much more productive. That is a great thing to hate. To sit and do nothing when a little application could at least change your world is one of the greatest non-violent sins.

Do you know successful people who are insecure? Maybe educated, intelligent people who act like fools because they think their husbands or wives are cheating on them? Do you know people who think everyone is stealing from them, so they spend most of their time at work looking for thieves? I'm not making this up. There are some really important people out there who are more concerned with who is dating who, what kind of car so and so is driving, how much money other people have, how far ahead someone else is getting, than time spent on important issues, like their heartbeat!

Please take care of yourself and try not to waste one more minute gossiping about unimportant, insecure crap. I'm not saying to be oblivious to your surroundings; I am saying not to spend your time trying to pull other people down so you will feel like you are closer to the top. You won't be. The only way to dissolve insecurity is build more confidence in yourself by achieving little personal goals. One day at a time and then suddenly you are out of the rut. I love that old Satchel Paige expression, "Don't look back, you might see who is gaining on you." Don't worry about who is doing what. It doesn't concern you. Do your best and focus on crossing the finish line, not where other people cross it. This doesn't apply to the sons of #%$@& who you might compete against that cheat. They get caught sooner than later, and if they hurt you by cheating, you ought to knock their block off!

I sure don't have all the answers; I only know what worked for me. My intention is to never hate anyone, anymore. I intend to be realistically confident about my abilities and try to improve that level whenever possible. Here are a few things I have found to be true. A person's height has nothing to do with how tall they stand. Strength has less to do with muscles than bathing suits have to do with polar bears. Always tell your doctor, lawyer and priest the truth; they all three are trying to save your life. Apprehension and fear are good. They certainly have a time and place in this life, and at the right time will serve you well.

I also know weak people like to intimidate other people because of insecurity. Maybe you didn't do anything wrong and you get chewed out just because the situation allows it. To hell with that! I'm not talking about a drill instructor who is trying to teach you to save your life. I'm not talking about a coach who knows you have more to give and is trying to safely get you to a new level. I'm talking about people who need to know that they are always in charge. They really are never in charge because they can't control themselves. I'm talking about hurting other people because they can or because they think they may be smarter than you or want to try something new. There are a thousand ways to say "no" without deliberately talking down to someone. There's no need to steal something just because you are not willing to work for it. There's never a reason to belittle and never a reason to steal. If you're starving, the county will feed you.

Don't read this and think it will be safe to roll up your sleeves and go challenge the Atlanta Falcons offensive line to a wrestling match. That isn't confidence, that's suicide. You have to have some common sense.

What have I been trying to get across here? Try not to hate other people. Do not let other people's hatred hold you down and keep you from being who you really are. Do not stay with people who want you to look bad so that they might look better. They won't, and it's a waste of your precious time. Insecurity and hate go hand in hand—quit holding hands with either of them.

—18—
The way I see it…
Every tragedy isn't avoidable;
every day wasted is

When I came out to Colorado, the people at EAS were good enough to help me find an apartment in Golden. They suggested a place near the headquarters, and after a week in a hotel, I moved into the apartment. It was, and probably still is, a nice place. It was a little expensive for me, but you get what you pay for, and this place had it all. There was a great pool, and it was quiet, clean, gated and had a well-equipped exercise room. That's where I was the day I met one of the most interesting, yet troubled people I have ever known.

There are so many rules and regulations in this life. Some only apply once or twice in the say 75 years or so that we will be here. Other rules and regulations are applied daily. I have written and do believe that one consistent, "never fail" rule is this: "We don't know from day to day what is going to happen." Remember, I said there are things in this life that we can control like what we eat, whom we date, if we go to church, etc. And there are things in this life we have absolutely no control over: the weather, with whom we fall in love, where we place when we have tried our best. Those things are out of our control. That's what this chapter is about, sort of.

In the apartment complex I spoke of, I had noticed a fellow a few times, and I couldn't exactly say what it was, but he was a little different than everybody else. I would see him sometimes walking early in the morning; nothing strange about that, a lot of people get up before sunrise and exercise, but this was different. It was as if he hadn't slept yet or something. I never spoke to him, and he never spoke to me. I would see him in the parking lot or maybe late at night having a light jog or maybe just out walking. That's all I can tell you about him. He was tall, quiet, well dressed (when he wasn't jogging), and I feel safe in saying he had something on his mind. As long as he didn't bother me, I didn't bother him, and life went on.

One Saturday afternoon, I went down to the workout room and there he was, alone. I started my workout, and he continued his, and we neither one spoke. We were both well aware of each other's presence; it ain't that big of a room, but again, he just wasn't somebody you would start shooting the breeze with. It began to get uncomfortably obvious that we were neither one going to speak.

After about half an hour, I was thinking about my workout and remember saying out loud and to no one in particular, "I'm getting too old for this." I have no idea why I blurted that out because I'm *not* too old for this, but I must have had an ache or pain or been out of breath or something, but I blurted it out anyway. I probably would have said it if no one had been in the room but me. He kinda chuckled and said, "Well you look in pretty good shape," and I said, "Yeah, but I have to work at it," and then I said something about wishing I had a beer, and he chuckled again, and I said something else and the conversation began.

We spent the next 20 or so minutes talking about EAS and Body-*for*-LIFE, and he was fairly knowledgeable about exercise, but like so many others, his experiences were from high school PE or running in boot camp. The supplement information was totally foreign to him. Somewhere along the way we both noticed the tension had disappeared and the conversation took off. I finally introduced myself, and if I live another hundred years, I will never forget the next thing that happened.

After I told him my name, we shook hands and he introduced himself. Said his name was John Dunaway, and then I asked him what he did for a living. I swear to whatever you hold sacred the temperature dropped about 10 degrees in that room, in that instant. He got that real hard look I'd always seen when he was walking by or out jogging, and I will tell you now it sort of scared me. It took him a second, almost like he wasn't sure he wanted to tell me, and then he said, "I'm the undersheriff here in Jefferson County."

Then I was the one who waited a second. It all of a sudden made sense. In a split second I understood his odd demeanor. It had been less than a month since he had responded to the call at Columbine High School.

I certainly remember writing (and it's in this book) about locking eyes with a 1941 Pearl Harbor survivor in Hawaii. I swear I could see that entire day in that veteran's eyes. It's almost frightening—no, it *is* frightening. And that exact same feeling came through John's eyes the second he knew that I also knew.

Since that day in the exercise room I have often talked to John about Columbine. He hasn't told me everything; some things are none of my business, some things he can't talk about, and some things he cannot bear to discuss. I think I understand. I certainly respect his and everyone else's privacy.

The Undersheriff is the chief operations officer, second in command in the county sheriff's office. He isn't like a vice president; he's more like the police chief of the department. I believe John was the second or third Command Police Officer on the scene, I'm not sure, nobody is, but he got there quick. He was the senior law-enforcement official in charge at the scene until the sheriff arrived. That's not a completely true statement; the people inside the school with the guns were in charge.

It's an unbelievably sad and tragic story. I was not there and am not in any way accusing or defending anyone's actions that day. That certainly isn't my job. My entire point is simply this: You have no idea what the rest of this day or what any tomorrows may hold. You might get up in the morning, shower, get dressed, walk outside and have your world and everyone else's world around you get turned upside-down on it's ass.

John Dunaway had a career as a police officer. He retired the first time as a police captain and holds a Ph.D. He was a professor, father and a public servant. He served in the Naval and Army Reserves and has done justice to the American way of life. He was called back into public service as the undersheriff of

Jefferson County, Colorado. Yet nothing prepared him or anyone else for April 20, 1999.

He got up that morning, got dressed, planned his day and went to the office. By noon, his life was forever changed. By noon, thousands of lives were forever changed. By noon, all of America was changed. I'm sorry that day happened, I'm sorry for all the children who suffered that day. I'm sorry for the families, students, teachers, the policemen and firemen and paramedics and doctors who had to put emotion on the backburner and tried to function with clear heads during a desperate and highly emotionally time.

We (EAS) went to Columbine at the appropriate time and offered any assistance we could. I think all of America did. We left 13 EAS hats in the park where most of America came and left flowers, ribbons, cards and tears. All the flowers, ribbons, and wreaths and the 13 EAS hats are gone now, but that's okay. We just wanted the Columbine family to know we cared and were there for them.

I can tell you that John Dunaway left a big piece of his heart there that day. I can't speak for anyone else who was there. I wasn't. You will have to ask them what that day was like. I have been fortunate enough to talk with John. I can tell you this: Live the rest of this day to the fullest degree. Live next week and every week thereafter "full bore." Cherish the people you love, and cherish every minute of every hour from now on. Don't miss one more deep breath because of something you think you can't control. Do not skip another workout or make another excuse to watch life from the bleachers if you are capable of getting in the game.

Every tragedy isn't avoidable; every wasted day is. There must be about a thousand phone companies out there and about a million phones. Call someone who cares about you and say something nice to him or her today. You never know when the last minute will be here. Do it before you can't do it.

I'm going to work out today and be thankful for every rep and every drop of sweat. Those innocent young men and women at Columbine and Oklahoma City, New York City and a hundred other places can't get a workout in today. I bet they wish they could. I bet their families wish they could. Get up, get off the couch and do something with the precious life you have left. Don't wait until you are 47 or 59 or until it's too late. Put this book down and go do something healthy. The book will be here when you get back.

I want to thank John Dunaway and all the nameless men and women who responded that day. I now know John well enough to say with conviction; he would give all he has to be able to relive that day. I know in my heart he would have gotten up that morning and drove 150 miles per hour to that school to prevent what happened. He just didn't know. You and I do not know what this day holds for us. I'm not going to throw my day away, I pray you don't throw yours away.

Because of Columbine and Oklahoma City and 9-11 and other similar events, we are much more aware of violence prevention, both in the schools, and at the work place. Don't wait for a stroke or heart attack to do a little "violence prevention" in your body.

142

Thank you, John, for your friendship. We both moved, and I don't see or talk to him as often. I won't forget those conversations. I won't forget talking with Deputy Cameron Carter, who stayed at the school after the incident for days, on his own time, helping out. There are good men and women who would have done all in their power to prevent this from happening. They didn't know it was going to happen. We, on the other hand, can look in the mirror and on our plate and see what is going to happen to our health.

Not sure how to end this chapter. Wish I could think of something brilliant or profound to write. I can't. I'm just sorry for the children and families of all tragedies. I am sad for all the public servants who dream about and think about having that day back to change the outcome. I'm sorry for the years I wasted doing nothing but throwing my health away. And I'm sorry for the person reading this simple book who doesn't get it, or the sad person who will throw his or her life away on poor health, for absolutely no reason at all. Amen.

—19—
The way I see it…
If you are only going to do one exercise
tomorrow, make it a walk with the Lord

It's Sunday morning. I woke up this morning and it was about 30 degrees outside. That's one big change since my transformation, but it isn't the biggest one. This is going to be hard to explain; it's kind of like sex—if you ain't had it, it's difficult to understand, but here goes.

I went back to church. I don't mean I went once and then returned; I actively got back in the church. I did it because of the Transformation Challenge and because God is very forgiving. What does that have to do with bodybuilding or good health or anything? Like I said, everything in your life improves when you are in control of *you*. Maybe I went to church this morning because I stayed sober last night. What did you do last night? I was home and in bed at a decent hour, and I repeat, I was sober.

For about 20 years I would have worked Saturday night until around midnight or so, and then I would really start winding down. Being in the bar and restaurant business, I was always serving other people. When I got off work, I went out and enjoyed seeing what other bars and restaurants were doing. I always looked for good staff and new recipes. It was usually drink recipes. Then, of course, I would eat and go back to my bars to close up for the night. I didn't do that last night. Understand, I was using my job as an excuse to be on the road and partying. There are plenty of smart people in this world in the bar business who do not go drinking every night.

My walk with the Lord is a very personal thing, and I don't need to explain it. I can tell you he welcomed me back with open arms. He loved me when I staggered up my driveway and tried unsuccessfully to cram my car key in the kitchen door lock at 3 a.m. He loved me that same night when I took my clothes off and slept in my underwear on the hood of my car. I know I hurt him on that and on several other nights. I couldn't be any more sorry, and he has forgiven me. I would also like to thank Ray Williams for coming over from next door at 6 a.m. and waking me up.

I don't know if you will get religion or not if you get your body healthy; how would I know that? Please believe with all your heart that it's one more good thing that happened to me. You and I are human, and we're going to slip again in this life. I still love the blues, and I'm going to try to go to another blues bar in this life. At 54 I'm single and still crazy about girls. You find me a blues bar, add a girl or two and a couple of cold beers, throw a shot of bourbon in there and that's right up my alley. The difference this time is I might have one beer instead of trying to drain the keg, or I might buy someone a drink instead of whipping out my credit card and setting up the bar. And this time I will be able to drive my own car home, remembering where I parked it and have an intelligent meal, take my supplements, get in my own bed and wake up with the sun. I can't tell you how much money I've saved by not having to buy a new wallet every three weeks. Trust me, this is a better life.

The fat and the bad habits were waiting on me to get rid of them, and they were waiting to get rid of me. You keep things around that you want and you get rid of things that you don't want. That's what a yard sale is. I kept a lot of leftover fattening food in the refrigerator along side a lot of cold beer. I kept the Lord in a dust-covered Bible on a shelf in a dust-covered corner. It may seem funny, but the more I got in control, the more the Lord came back into my life. Welcome home!

I have no idea if anyone will buy or read this book; all I can do is write what I know while there's still some air in the balloon. You certainly can take it or leave it. Believe me, I'm going to be human while I'm on this earth. I intend to have another drink someday. I hope to eat a plate of barbeque and another pork chop or two. What will be different is that I'll stay sober and not try to become like the pig that I'm eating. I'll never be on the level with Billy Graham, the Pope or any other religious leader. I wouldn't even try. What we can do is get some sort of religion in our lives and try to live a little cleaner mentally, physically and spiritually.

I know a couple of people who are dangerous folks. They are capable of creating a great deal of violence in a short period of time. Usually a short period of time is all it takes. The three or four I have in mind are very much at peace with a higher being. I can think of professional athletes who have excelled in their field who proclaim their love for the Lord proudly. They keep their bodies fit, and spiritually they are at peace. They make their living in a rough trade but nonetheless love their Lord. I listened to boxing champion Evander Holyfield give his testimony, and Mr. Olympia Lee Haney was on television giving his, too. We all know a lot of sports figures who are at peace with God.

There's nothing silly about getting right with whatever God you believe in. I am not ashamed of getting back in the church; I am ashamed of how long I was gone.

—20—
The way I see it…
When you say "No" today, you'll be able to say "Yes!" a thousand times in the future

For some people graduation comes early, for others late, and for some never. We graduate from elementary school, junior high and high school, then for some of us, it's college. I don't know how you will graduate or when, or even if you will. But you will know it when it happens.

For some of us it's the death of a loved one, our mother or father, or maybe a child. At that instant we know how fragile and precious life is. For some of my friends it was Vietnam. They went there young, fresh-faced soldiers and then came home completely different people. Some didn't come home at all. Graduation can happen at the birth of a child or a marriage or even a divorce.

Having money doesn't measure character. There are some bad people who win the lottery. That's not graduation. Working hard a long time and losing everything is. Getting a diploma is wonderful, but there are some college graduates who know less after four years than they did when they started. I think graduation in life is the day something happens to you and your values change for the better.

Mine was pretty simple. It was the day I was able to say the word, "No!" That's it. Told you it was simple. I said, "No!" to most everything that was bad for me. I didn't want to hurt anyone's feelings, but they began hearing the word "No" a lot. Can you say, "No!"?

You may find your friends leaving you when you say, "No" a lot. As a matter of fact, you probably will. That's unfortunate, but stand your ground. It's like loaning money. We have all loaned a friend money and we sometimes never see the money or the friend again. Now I just say, "No" and will have a 50/50 chance of at least seeing the friend again.

Don't go along just because the crowd is going. Don't do anything that's bad for you simply because you want to be accepted. Accepted by what? A group of people who are doing something stupid; run instead. Anyone who offers to assist you in committing a crime, putting something bad in your body, breaking training or jeopardizing your freedom in any way, is not your pal. Say "No!" Like I said, if you can't go with someone as good as you, go alone.

I'm completely aware that this is a little different chapter, but remember I said my transformation was more about what I quit doing than what I started doing. I graduated from always saying, "Yes" to another round of drinks. From saying, "Yes" to a 3 a.m. breakfast and then bed, to learning how to say, "No." It's a small word but powerful enough to save your life.

If you're standing at the altar and absolutely unsure of what you are "fixing" to do, you better say, "No." I promise if you say, "No" today, you will be able to say, "Yes!" a thousand times in the future. Say "No" for 84 days and if you stick to it, you will be "Yes, yes, yessing!" for the rest of your life.

—21—
A Road Less Traveled

Step 1. Realize you are in a rut and make your mind up to get out of it. Step 2. Buy the Body-*for*-LIFE Book and follow the directions. When you finish the first 12 weeks take a week off from training and then do the Body-*for*-LIFE a second time if you wish. You will be better at it the second time around. (If I were you I would enter the Million dollar Body-*for*-LIFE Challenge at the same time. Somebody is going to win it)! Step 3. Get on a program that allows you to Live Life and maintain the healthy new Body you have. We will call it Day 85. Three easy and simple and do-able steps to Freedom and Great Health and Life!

Please think about what I am writing here. This is so simple. I know in my heart somewhere someday a very famous and intelligent person whom thousands and thousands of people listen to, is going to say, "Porter was right, all you have to do is want it." Listen close, the carb control protein bars and Myoplex shakes and AdvantEdge RTD's and the new Body-*for*-LIFE bars and Ready-to-Drink shakes taste so good that you can have your cake and eat it to. The only reason anybody in the world can not get healthy is because they do not want to be healthy.

Have you been drinking a 2 scoop ice cream milk shake everyday? Change it for a strawberry Myoplex shake. If there is anyone reading this who can't eat a Body-*for*-LIFE bar instead of a real piece of chocolate cheesecake, then they Do Not want to get fit.......that simple. You can have a wedge of apple pie with scoops of ice cream or you can have a Apple Cinnamon Delite Myoplex bar......the choice is yours and the only difference is about 40 grams of fat and 45 carbohydrates and about a million calories. Want more honesty? Have some. I work for EAS and we make Body-*for*-LIFE bars and Ready-to-Drink shakes and EAS Myoplex, AdvantEdge and Carb Control bars, so those are the ones I eat. Remember, its almost 8 years later and I am still under 200 pounds down over 50 pounds from 264 pounds in 1997. Now I would never say and have never been asked to say, other bars and shakes are not good. They sure might be. I just don't know, I don't use them. I like to leave the dance with the gal I come with. EAS and Body-*for*-LIFE got me here and the shakes and RTDs and nutrition bars I do use have kept me healthy and fit and I am going to keep on using them till I can't swallow. Use ours, use theirs, use something!

By now you know Eric Shrieves and I ask him to help me put together a work out plan for after the 12 week Challenge. He did it (named it Day 85) and it is in the next few pages. Before I turn you over to him, I , from the bottom of my heart, want you to read about 2 other work out programs that are beyond anything I could ever imagine or attempt. Take the time to read these two little stories and then answer a honest question for me. The question is at the end of the stories.

I have met a lot of interesting people while traveling all over the world for EAS. The Body-*for*-LIFE Challenge is in 64 countries and the book is in 16 or 17 languages. There are some amazing stories out there and some unbelievable training but when it comes to the Body-*for*-LIFE Program, these 2 stand out more then any other work out schemes or training programs or what ever you want to call it I have ever heard of. Lets just say for the sake of conversation that you set aside 8 or 10 or 12 weeks to do some sort of exercise and diet routine. Try these 2 on for size.

I would consider it an honor to introduce you to Jim Schneeberger and Hugh "Duke" Dearing. We will start with Jim. As I said part of my job as Director of Body-*for*-LIFE is to travel the world and hand out prizes and rewards and Championships for jobs well done. I was in London England a year or two ago and was getting ready for the United Kingdom Night of Champions. Little did I know I would meet a gentleman that night who would have such an important impact on my Life.

We were setting up an auditorium for the evening events and naturally I hardly knew anyone working there, I'm not from England. There were light crews and television crews and sound people and one guy with a tie on who was by himself setting out chairs. He was a little overdressed to be a "roadie" but nontheless was working with a purpose. Those were the straightest rows of chairs I have ever seen.

The United Kingdom Grand Champion Female that year

was a beautiful lady named Gabi Schneeberger. When I finally worked my way over to the guy in the tie, I introduced myself and extended my hand. He spoke, damn near broke my hand when he shook it and said he was Jim Schneeberger, Gabi's husband. We made small talk and went on with our business. We had a great evening, recognized several Champions, had guest speakers and just had a big time. After the event, we went to a celebration dinner and then a few of us made it back to the hotel for a night cap. Me and this fellow Jim were 2 of the last people at the bar and I struck up a conversation about my hand still stinging from the handshake. He laughed and I laughed and we got to talking.

We got around to our histories and he mentioned he had served in the Army during the Rhodesian War. I of course ask his job and he casually mentioned he had been a Selous Scout. Okay, great, what did they do? He went on to sort of explain and it sounded a little like our Rangers or Green Berets but not exactly. He thought it might be better if he sent me a book written by one of the Scouts. I like reading about the military and police and history, so I promised I would read it and we moved on to other topics.

To be completely honest (and I am) I forgot about the book. I went on to some other country and some other Champion and back to the states and to hundreds of e-mails and phone calls and letters. One day a package came and inside was a promise kept by Jim Schneeberger. The package contained a note from Jim thanking me for my visit and it was a pleasure to meet me and Gabi was doing well and as fit as ever. There was also a book written by Lt. Col. Ron Reid-Daly. "PAMWE CHETE" Legend of the Selous Scouts. And very much like a book I had read years ago "Jaws", I could not set this book down. I read it and re-read it and sent it back to Jim to be signed. He was kind enough to answer my prayers and sent it to Col. Reid-Daly and the Col. signed it. I know what I am saying here when I report to you that I value this signed copy of "PAMWE CHETE" as much as I do my Championship ring or jacket.

Today when I speak at a Police or Fire or Sheriff's Department I beg the listeners to get a copy of "PAMWE CHETE" and read it. You should to! With Jim's permission I would like to share a day in the life of a Scout during training......let me take it a step further. I will "compare" a day in the life of a Scout with a day in the life of a chase lounge lizard who calls and tells me he or she just can't do the Body-*for*-LIFE Challenge, it's just too hard.

Welcome to Camp: A little test to get to the training area. This training was done in the jungle in Africa...freezing at night and well in the 90's during the day.

Start with a 15 mile run in full combat gear with weapon and ammo.

Stand in a lake (in full gear) up to your neck with your rifle held above water for 1 hour. If the rifle goes in the water you start over.

Sleep on ground with all your gear while still wet. No food. On Welcome to Camp Day, 20 men quit.

Day 1.
5:45am till 7:30am.

-3x 15 minute runs with 10 second full burst of speed run each minute. Do not stop.
-50 reps of Jumping jacks and then 1 set to failure.
-50 push ups then 100 push ups then 1 set to failure.
-2x28 yard run with partner on your back.
-50 sit ups then 100 sit ups then 1 set to failure.
-Bunny hops or duck walks 4x 10 yards.

4:45pm till 5:30pm.
- Rope Course. 40 foot rope suspended 40 feet above a patch of thorn bushes, no water, no safety net, just thorn bushes. Try not to fall. Had to pull yourself along rope with hands and feet. No food all day.

Day 1.
- Body-*for*-LIFE: 20 minutes of HIT cardio. 6 meals.

Day 2.
6:00am till 7:30 am.
- Log PT. 5 men per log. Log weight: about 220 pounds
- 30 minute run with log.
- 60 minutes of exercise with log: 25 left shoulder lifts 25 right shoulder lifts 1 set to failure.
- 50 sit ups with log on thighs 1 set to failure.
- Pull ups. 1 man did 50 (5x10) pull ups while other 4 held log over their head.
- Chin ups. Same as pull ups.
- Bench press with log. 50 (5x10) then 1 set to failure.

- Leg lifts 50 then 1 set to failure.
- Squats. 50 with log behind thighs then 1 set to failure.
- Log lifts. 50 reps behind neck 1 set to failure.

* As men dropped out there were less men per log. The ending number of men was 3 per log. The number of sets and reps never decreased. The log just got heavier per man.

Still Day 2.
Noon till 1 or 2:00pm. Repeat Day 1. Exercises. Run, jumping jacks, etc. Still no food.

Day 2.
- Body-*for*-LIFE. 45 minutes of weight lifting. 6 meals.

Day 3.
- Exercise for 1 1/2 hours 3 times a day.
- Rope course every other day. Log course every other day.
- Cross country 10 to 15 miles. (Remember this was in the jungle)
- Speed march with packs 18 to 20 miles
- Exercise same as day1.
- Night Marches with sandbags 15 miles
- Speed runs 8 to 15 miles
- Airstrip runs. Running up and down a landing strip with weapons and sandbags until failure.
- Boxing matches once a week. If not enough aggression was shown, you had to box a bigger heavier opponent.

- For fun and relaxation: Rugby played on a sandy dry river bed.
- Punishment for lack of aggression or other foul up: Climb a 50 foot rope tied to a Baobab tree and ring a bell. No bell, climb again.
- Punishment for serious offense: Everyone in squad had to perform all daily activities with an additional 20 pound bag of sand.

All of this training was done the first 5 days on NO FOOD! After first 5 days meals were rationed to 1 meal every 3 days.

Day 3.
-Body-*for*-LIFE: Repeat 20 minutes of HIT cardio. 6 meals.

Please don't say "Well why doesn't Porter just go join the Selous Scouts" That would be ridiculous. I am simply trying to show all of you and myself that the Body-*for*-LIFE Challenge is nothing compared to some of the training that has gone on and goes on in this world. The Body-*for*-LIFE Challenge is so simple! It is so easy to do if you want it. And the other good news is that the Maintaince program is EASIER then the 12 week Challenge. I have done them both…thousands of people have done them and continue to do them and it is easy, easy, easy. By the way did I mention that the first meal the Scouts got after 5 days was a half rotted monkey? Did I mention they all ate it without question. It is amazing what you will eat when you are hungry. Do you know what Jim told me his greatest fear was on "Night Training" in the jungle? Being eaten by a lion.

Let's see! We work out 3 or 4 times a week for less then an hour in a air conditioned gym with the television on. We wear the latest gym fashions and shower and blow dry our hair and put on cologne and have a shake or healthy protein bar before and after the work out. If you are a woman in a gym you need not worry about the lions attacking you, just watch out for the wolf lurking by the water cooler!

The Scouts may not be as famous as the SAS or our US Navy SEALS but they cut as wide a path and for a cause they believed in. You can't become a Scout today, that window is closed forever. When I do not feel like training or doing my cardio, I think of a lot of reasons and people who help me get off my tired old rear-end and get to that air-conditioned gym. You find your heroes and you think of what they have been through and what they have willingly endured for their cause. Your cause should be to improve your health and Live this wonderful Life to the fullest. 3 or 4 or even 2 workouts a week, 20 minutes of cardio a couple of times a week and a completely free day to sit on our butts and eat crap all day if we want to…

I guess some people are right, it's just too hard..

In a letter Jim wrote me he said he would have been proud to serve with me in the Scouts and had no doubt that I would have made it through the Selection Course. I would like to publicly say he is dead wrong. I do not believe there is any way on God's green earth that I could have withstood that self inflicted pain. I am not that strong. What an Honor it is that he would have thought I could have made it. He sent me a shirt with the Silver Osprey patch and the words Selous Scouts on the pocket. I can't wear it, I didn't earn it. I am a better man for having met Jim and Gabi and a better man for having learned of the Legend of the Selous Scouts. There is a show on cable television where you get to live one of your dreams. If I won it I would certainly consider asking if I could have dinner with Jim and Gabi and Col. Ron Reid-Daly and the members of the Scouts, except this time I would know better then to shake any hands! Now, go read the book.

Meet Hugh "Duke" Dearing......but be glad you didn't run into him in the jungles of South East Asia. More than likely his would have been the last face you might have seen on this earth. I've known Duke for 30 years and it took a lot of begging to get this report from him. He seems to think it is for a good cause so he wrote out a couple of pages. I reduced it for the sake of time. It is a strong message and worth reading. If after reading Duke's work-out and reading Jim's work-out, we think we don't have time or the program Eric put together is too hard or takes too long, then we just don't want it. It's that simple.

Time: late 1960's and early 70's. Place: Camp Geiger just outside of Camp Lejeune, North Carolina. Reason: United States Marine Corps Recon Training. At the time there were only three Force Recon Companies in the Corps. Each company consisted of about 250 Marines. This included headquarters staff of about 25 and U.S. Navy Hospital Corpsmen. Each company was divided into 15 man Recon Platoons.

Let's take an average day in the Life of a candidate for the

160

title Recon Marine. Reveille (some guy blasting a bugle in your ear) was at 5:00a.m. on the second. All personnel had exactly 45 minutes to get up, make their bunk, shave, shower, brush any teeth they had, dress, have the barracks squared away and be in formation at 5:45 a.m. in front of the headquarters building. The headquarters building was not where they slept so you can surmise they had to run double time to get there by 5:45 a.m.

Now for a little PT. (Physical Training). As a company and altogether they did jumping jacks, side straddle hops, push ups, sit ups, bend and thrust, and pull ups. This usually lasted 25 or 30 minutes (sometimes more, you just never knew) but it depended on who was leading the PT that morning. After those exercises the company went on a 5 or 8 or 10 mile run. Again, this was always done in formation. After the run which always ended back at the headquarters, the candidates were dismissed for breakfast. It didn't matter if you had run 5 or 10 miles that morning, you had to wash and eat and be squared away by 8:00a.m. for daily assignments. How nice of the instructors? Some days Duke had 20 minutes and other days he had 5. Nothing like a little positive pressure.

On with the day..No matter where you were going, you ran. No matter if you were alone or two of you or 15, you ran. You only slowed down to salute an officer, then start running again. If you were going to parachute training you ran the 3 miles to the landing field, boarded the aircraft, went airborne, jumped out of the perfectly good airplane, landed, gathered your gear as well as the deployed parachute and then ran (not walked) back to the gathering area.

Maybe you would go to Rubber Boat Training that day. Those exercises included: lifting the boat, carrying the boat, launching, paddling and landing the boat. Stands to reason if this is done in water, then all the running and carrying and loading was done in sand. Makes it a little harder. Maybe then a candidate got to go swimming. This consisted of diving, swimming, out of the water, sit ups, running in sand, back in the water, more swimming and about a thousand flutter kicks. Those were just the exercises, after all that there was Scuba training.

Since wars are not on the clock and don't much pay attention to the calendar, this training had to be done both day and night, roasting and freezing. When you are out on a Recon patrol, it happens mostly at night. Unlike Jim Schneeberger and his small problem with being eaten by a lion, Duke and his team members only had to be concerned with alligators and rattlesnakes and cotton mouth water moccasins and every other kind of poisonous snake in Eastern North and South Carolina. Sometimes the snakes were scared the Marines would eat them.

Duke was a Marine first and then a Paris Island Drill Instructor. He went on to be a Recon Marine and served several tours in Vietnam. He was given a battlefield promotion to Lieutenant and received numerous citations and ribbons for his service. He has a couple of Purple Hearts and a broken one for a job left undone 30 years ago. He lives in North Carolina and has a web site somewhere on the internet. Maybe someday you will be fortunate enough to meet him and ask him how he got the nickname "Duke". It is a pretty interesting story.

The Marine Corps has a long and proud tradition of being fit.

162

If a different branch of the service had a requirement of 10 pull ups for admission, then the Corps required 20. I won't get into which branch is best or which branch won any war. That friendly argument will go on forever. I know this. When a soldier gives his or her Life for their country, they were the best that day from the best branch from the best country in the world. A medic on the front lines is equal to the soldier being saved. The nurse in a makeshift hospital saving a life is equal in every way to the patient.

This is my book and in my book, every man and woman who ever put on a uniform and served the United States of America is a hero. The Army Rangers and the Navy Seals and the Air Force Survival School in Florida, all true heroes. Want a dose of real training, go join the Green Berets. Try the 82nd Airborne or the 101st. The Coast Guard cannot be forgotten, I have met a few of these Americans and don't think I have the stomach for what they do. I watched a film of their ship going out to save some boaters and the ship was coming out of the water on every other wave. I couldn't do it no matter how much training was offered.

I think Jim Schneeberger and Hugh "Duke" Dearing were cut from the same cloth. They heard a calling and answered it. They wanted to be the best they could and to earn the title "SELOUS SCOUT" or "RECON MARINE" a price had to be paid. It was paid in full. What a priceless Honor to call both these men my Friends. I thank them for helping me with this book.

Well, here it is in a nutshell. Remember I said there would be a question at the end of these two stories? This is the question: Do you really want to be healthier? Do you really want it or not? Do you want some expensive surgery that forces you to do what you can't do yourself? Jim Schneeberger could not find one human being in this world who could go through the training for him. It doesn't work that way. I am no more a Scout because I know Jim then you are. He did the work and he earned the title. Duke left the Corp after 11 years of service but he will forever hold the title "Force Recon Marine". He earned it. Nobody on this earth did it for him, nobody. I couldn't get through the Reserves and can not call myself something I did not earn. Neither can you. Did Arnold Palmer's caddy take the shot for Arnold? Of course not. He stood by and he offered Arnold help and opinion and was with him all the way but for Arnold Palmer to win the Master's, he had to make the putt. Probably very few people reading this will ever earn the titles we have been writing about but anybody reading this can earn the title Body-*for*-LIFE Champion. It may not hold the Respect of "Scout" or "Recon Marine" but it has Value. It is your Life we are talking about here. What could be more valuable? NOTHING- NOTHING- NOTHING. Nothing in this world is as valuable as your health. Do you want it or not? That's the question I wanted to ask.

I guess I should turn you over to Eric now. I can not add or subtract one thing from the first 12 weeks of the Body-*for*-LIFE. I didn't use the free day, I stayed on the program 7 days a week but that's just me. Maybe that's why Jim thought I might make it through the Scouts. I wasn't going to give up. You don't have to be as fanatic as I was. Maybe you won't need to be. That is up to you. Anyway I have maintained (along with thousands of others) a pretty good level of health and fitness over the past 7 years. Here is how this one Champion did it. You can do it my way or any way you want. Just please do something.

Well there you have it. Recognize you are in a rut, get out of the rut and stay out of the rut. The rut doesn't ever go away, its always there. Anywhere there is a road there is a rut and it is up to you to keep it between the ditches and out of the rut. There are so many ways to get unhealthy and just as many ways to get healthy again. My mind always goes back to the Jared Horomona, a Inspirational Champion from New Zealand and Paul Sullivan and Jeff Kundert and the Vicky Magnum's of this world. People who have been dealt some unfair cards from an unjust deck yet because of class, character, and self-respect, Class: who you choose to associate with, Character: what you do in this Life, Self-respect: what you refuse to do in this Life, they took control of their lives. They fought back and out of the rut. They were sick and tired of the "Comfort of their Misery" and did something about it.

My buddy Eric told me once "The difference in a decision and a choice is: You decide to get well and then you make the right choices." Life is going to end and we will go to eternity in a Gold Cadillac or we might go walking, but either way we are going. Until then why not climb those mountains and swim in the ocean and hike and breath and live every minute you can? Wouldn't it be better to leave this earth having experienced some of the things other people find so much pleasure in. Do you really want to draw your last breath sitting in front of a television and be found the next morning with a spoon in your hand and a half eaten gallon of ice-cream melted down the front of your chest?

There was a time years ago, I might have been found with a dozen empty beer cans at my death bed. Me and thousands of others from all over the world made the "Decision" to change what the Paramedics and Firemen find in our homes when that day comes and come it will! You want the Coroner to get a hernia carrying you out of your house? Keep on eating. You want to waste away to nothing so you can fit in a size 1, keep on starving yourself. Don't you see, it's up to you. Nobody else can make you be healthy or stop you from being healthy, it's your decision and choice. Maybe my greatest dream is the day I'm walking through an Airport or bookstore or somewhere and you come up to me all smiles and say, "Hey Porter, I'm Finally Fit, I made it" Only you can make that dream come true...

—The Last Word—
The way I see it...
We all have the power to change,
and no one can ever take that away

One last thought before I let you go. If you're the reader who doesn't think he or she can do this, you're wrong. *You can!* I can't be there to look you in the eye, and Bill Phillips wasn't there that night he spoke to me from his magazine. I honestly believe if he had, he would have begged me to change my ways. That's what I'm doing here and now.

I don't want to let you go. If simply asking you one more time to please get up off the couch and get healthy and fit will convince you, then I'm asking. If the people around you are not telling you the truth about your condition, then I am. Remember that good health is the slowest way to death. I'm begging you to stay alive and live alive a little longer. I like that, "live alive," as opposed to living dead.

This book obviously wasn't about exercise or diets or nutrition.

As I said, there are plenty of good books out there about that, and they were written by people smarter than me. I'm not an expert at anything except getting off the couch and getting back into life. Maybe this book was about recognizing you are on the couch, and whatever got you there is keeping you there. It isn't a self-help book; I'm not a doctor, and I don't have an M.D. I don't have an M.S. or an MBA, or any other letters behind my name. I'm a regular guy with a high school education who changed his miserable life. That's what this book is about, changing.

Get up off your rear-end and go do something. Step up to the plate and push yourself away from the plate. This book is about admitting you're in a rut, wanting out, and finally getting the hell out it.

What is it you want in this life? Is it money? Money is a wonderful thing. I am convinced money will not make miserable people happy, but it will make them comfortable. If making money makes you happy, then go for it. Nothing wrong with that. If making pies makes you happy, then make pies for a living. Nothing wrong with that either. Some of us enjoy selling cars. Some of us enjoy going to work at a machine shop every morning. I wouldn't like either, but that's okay. Some people love it. In my wildest dreams I could not imagine slicing someone open to operate on their insides, but a lot of people go through 10 years of medical school to get that privilege.

What do you do? Do you love your job? When you go home after work, do you have a good feeling about what you did all day? There's no right or wrong answer here. Some people do a job that's necessary, although they may not like it, and some people do a job they like that may not be necessary. Some folks work at something that they may be good at but can't stand doing. There are all types of situations. I was a good bar manager, I just ain't sure if I was doing any good.

Where am I going with this? About two days ago it finally dawned on me what I'm supposed to do with my life. It has taken 54 years, but in the middle of a conversation, I knew the answer. I was a little long in coming around to it, but like salvation, you know it when it happens. What a revelation!

The past few months I've had the privilege and honor of representing EAS and the Body-*for*-LIFE Challenge on an ABC daytime television tour across America. We've been in a dozen cities, one Saturday after another, nonstop. I usually get to town a few days before the mall appearance and stay a few days afterwards so I can visit our retailers. Have to admit the 12-weeks schedule was a little tough at times, but I have successfully gone through other 12-week "challenges."

On one of these trips I returned to a hotel and flopped down on a chair, exhausted. It had been a 14-hour day of standing on my tired old feet, talking, answering questions, looking at pictures and doing what I do for the company. I had been in three states (all close to each other) and probably talked to 400 people. No exaggeration. I was beat. All I wanted to do was get a quick meal and some rack time. My partner that day was our field rep for New England, and he was stuck with driving me that day, and he was beat also. Things didn't work out exactly like we planned. As soon as we sat down a nice young lady approached the table. She knew me and knew about EAS, and she was doing the Body-*for*-

LIFE Challenge. She worked at the hotel where I was staying and asked if I would sign her Body-*for*-LIFE book and answer a few questions. She said she didn't mean to interrupt and if she was a bother, she would excuse herself. She was overweight and confided she had been overweight all her life. And on and on and on...

What do you think my answer was? You got it. I asked her to join us and spent the next hour and a half listening, answering questions, while giving all the encouragement I could think of. I wiped away her tears, pleaded with her to stay on course, comforted her, and, I pray, gave her some hope.

Now I'm not a combat medic or Florence Nightingale or Mother Teresa. As a matter of fact, I haven't always been real nice to everybody I had to help out of a bar. But then again, they weren't always nice to me. We reap what we sow. Anyway, there was nothing more important than listening and talking with her. She really wanted help, and I know in my heart she was sincere. I don't know if she got it, but it was my obligation and honor to give her the message.

I don't know if it's better to talk to a thousand people or one at a time. I have done both and as long as somebody "gets it," then it has been worth the effort. When the young lady got up to go home, the gentleman with me shook his head and said, "How do you do it, how do you get so excited about this time after time all day long?" Right then I knew what I was supposed to do with my life. By answering his question, the light and the truth came shining through. It always does. It always will. Remember Harvey Miller (I wrote about him in a previous chapter)? He

170

was the truth guy. The truth came out in that one second.

I'm simply the messenger and the message is simple. You can, can, *can* change your life and redirect it anyway you want to. When people look at me, the (as Bill put it) "Real-World Proof" is standing in front of them. As long as I go on making intelligent choices, I will continue to be "Real-World Proof." The people who say I didn't turn my life around in 84 days and it can't be done are 100 percent absolutely right. The men and women who come up to me cloaked in their misery and say there is no way to make the changes me and thousands of other people did are also 100 percent exactly right. It didn't take 84 days—it took about one-millionth of a second. That's all. In that millionth of a second, I made my mind up to get healthy. It just took my body 84 days to catch up.

That, my friend, is my calling and mission in this life. To tell every person who is cloaked in and wallowing in misery that they can be free in as much time as it takes to say "I am finished with the life I am dying in"—one-millionth of a second. The mind leads and the body follows. When I am dead and gone and long forgotten, my conscience will be clear. I took the time to write it all down and spent my last dime to record the message. "You can change your life if you want to."

I sorta know how a team of doctors and nurses feel after they stand for hours and hours and save a life. Maybe that's how preachers like my grandfather felt when they converted a person for God. I guess that's how a firefighter and policeman or policewoman feels when they stand in freezing rain and snow, directing traffic and fighting a fire that's raging out of control.

Maybe the feeling they get, knowing they saved a life (the most precious thing on this earth) is far greater than the simple little paycheck they take home. When the police write a ticket, I don't much care for them. But when they tromp through woods and thorns and swamps for hours and hours looking for a lost child, or when they run up to and pull people from burning cars and wrecks, then they are heroes far beyond that which my words can describe.

Never, ever in this world would I put my small contribution on their level. But when one person walks up and asks for my advice or some sort of inspiration, there's nothing any more important in this world than trying to help that person. If talking to me or one of the other Champions is what it takes to unlock those very real-to-you, yet imaginary chains, then let that be my calling for the rest of my life. I don't know if it will be at EAS or if it won't, but it will be my job, somehow or the other, for the rest of my life.

When I started writing this book, it was to tell people that, "The difference between a rut and the grave is the depth." You can get out of a rut, but we ain't getting out of the grave. Since I wrote all this, I have learned something new, and that is what to do with my life. Bill's job was to get me or anyone else listening off the couch. Eric's job was to show me the way, and my job (along with all the other Champions) is to convince unsure people that they can change their self-induced poor health. We are all potential "Real-World Proof." All that the nine other Champions and I did was go before you, so that you can feel safe following in our footsteps. Those footsteps are imbedded on safe, stable, sure ground.

Are you reading this book in 2004 or 2005, or maybe it's 2010? I don't know when you will read it. Whatever the date, the message remains the same. No steroids, no quick-acting pill, no sauna, no rubdown, no nothing except desire, faith and belief. Then you must stay within the boundaries. Don't tell me you can't do it, you can. Other than an act of nature, there is no failure other than not wanting to succeed and not willing to give up temporary rewards for long-term improvement. I don't have great genetics or some secret agent plan that I'm not sharing. You can come live with me if you want to. All that I do and all that I am is open to the public to see and share. What I did was drop 74 pounds of unhealthy fat and add about 10 pounds of muscle all in about 14 weeks. The magic formula was to stop cramming crap down my throat and start exercising. How difficult was that?

—Appendix A—

Congratulations on seeing the Challenge through. Whew! Great job, but guess what ?- Actually it's never really "over" if you want to continue to reap the benefits of improving your state of physical and mental well-being. One recommendation is to now take one week to ten days off completely from any disciplined approach to fitness. That's not done to encourage total laziness and indifference. Instead, it's done to allow the body's muscular and nervous systems a chance to replenish and refresh themselves. Enjoyable activities (cycling, walking, tennis, swimming, etc.) can still be pursued, just take a welcomed break from the discipline and the intense aspect of vigorous training. You'll come back with a renewed sense of purpose, and a body ready to feel vital once again.

If your efforts have gotten you where you want to be in terms of enhancing muscularity, a loss of body-fat, and an increase in cardio-respiratory fitness, then you will want to consider a maintenance approach to wellness. However, most people, if they're being totally honest, would like to take it a step further-there's certainly nothing wrong with that! As a matter of fact, it's the beauty of pursuing fitness-we can always improve! Again, for those seeking more of a maintenance approach, here goes;

The vital concerns and success of this process are; (as many of you may have figured out) genetic predisposition (some of us tend to be naturally more lean and muscular while others struggle with having more abundant fat storage cells and slower metabolic rates), volitional effort and motivation, proper exercise movement selection and execution, regulating the volume and frequency of the workouts, adequate intensity of effort, sleep quality, proper pre-/post -workout nutrition, etc.

Since each of us is unique in our ability to adapt to the stress of exercise (both proper and improper), there really is no "cookie cutter" approach to exercise that applies to all. What does apply to each of us, is the realization that it takes a focused, determined, consistent effort to create a positive change, and adequate rest and nutritional support to allow for the change(s). The great news, however, is that it doesn't require a 24 hour per day "obsession" to be successful. As a matter of fact, you should now be able to incorporate a more "real world" approach to being fit! You should also be more aware of exercise movement efficiency, as well as finding some of the healthy foods and dietary applications that you most enjoy.

Your goal is not to see just how much exercise you can perform (or tolerate), it is rather, to find the least amount of truly productive effort/work in a given time frame. In that regard, you will avoid unproductive, repetitive efforts and avoid an over-training scenario, thereby devoting more of the body's resources for recovery and compensation from the workout(s).

Train somewhat briefly, with adequate intensity and focus, and then get out of the gym. As Porter says, "it's a work-out, work and get out". Your next priority is now on proper nourishment, sleep quality and tranquility, to further reduce exercise-induced stress!

While in the gym, you should choose exercise movements that will most favorably recruit the greatest amount of muscle fibers. Through that goal you will be getting the most "bang for your buck", so to speak. Minimize the use of so-called "isolation" movements-they don't truly exist anyway. The most one can hope for is muscle "emphasis", not muscle isolation, since all muscles, while performing their work, engage fully (not merely a specific portion of the target muscle is engaged). Next, choose a repetition scheme to fit your goals. If seeking to mainly increase your strength levels rather than acquiring more muscular mass, then training with low reps and longer rest periods between sets using heavier resistance (3-5 reps, for example) should fit the bill. If an increase in muscular size along with some increase in strength is your goal, then using a weight that calls for approximately 6-12 reps with about 1 minute's rest are for you. Higher reps (15-20 and above), with shorter rest periods between sets, will increase muscular endurance performance. Each repetition scheme should see you performing proper execution of form (controlled reps, with a greater emphasis on the lowering (negative or eccentric portion) of the repetition, while seeking to go to near- positive "failure" with each work set. In other words, the final rep (or two) of the set should be difficult to perform. If it's not, then the actual weight used for the prescribed number of reps is not heavy enough!

In terms of the amount or volume of work sets to be performed with each workout, there is actually no "ideal" number that is etched in stone. How often one chooses to train and even the number of body parts that are addressed in the workout are but 2 examples of proper considerations. Again, your particular and unique tolerance for exercise stress is a limiting factor. After a proper, but not too extensive, warming up period-(don't turn the warm-up into an actual work-out of sorts), then as few as 2 or 3 focused and intense sets of 2 movements per body part could be sufficient. If choosing instead to use a greater selection of movements for each target muscle group, then even fewer total sets per body part may be called for. You can and should periodically "change it up" a bit. Both the workout and dietary approaches will thrive best with periodic unpredictability.

Consider these movement choices as examples for maximizing training efficiency.

LEGS- Squat, Leg Press, Leg extension (quadricep dominant movements) Stiff legged deadlift or Leg curl (standing or lying)-(hip dominant movements)

CALVES- Donkey calf raise, Standing 1 leg calf raise (w/ a singular dumbbell), Seated calf raise

BACK- Pullup, Barbell Bent Row, or 1 Arm dumbbell Row

CHEST- Decline dumbbell bench press, Flat bench press or Incline dumbbell bench press

SHOULDERS- Standing shoulder press, Incline lateral raise, or Standing bent-over rear dumbbell raise

TRICEPS- Dips, Tricep Extension, Tricep pushdown

BICEPS- Standing Barbell Curl (straight bar), Incline dumbbell Curl, or Hammer Curl

ABDOMINALS- Crunch, Jack knife sit-up, Hanging hip raise, Reverse crunch, twisting crunch

There are obviously many more movement selections that can be utilized, but for making best use of your time in the gym, migrate toward those movements that will allow you to use more weight and thus innervate more muscle fibers. You can reference www.bodyforlife.com for an interactive exercise movement demonstration. To maximize your performance and also minimize muscle breakdown/loss, both pre-and post- workout nutritional concerns are important, with emphasis on utilizing a quality protein and moderate carbohydrate before training (such as the new Body-*for*-LIFE Ready-to-Drink formulas) and later consuming a quick-acting protein and carbohydrate combination beverage immediately (Myoplex, for example or the new Myoplex Sport Bar, both of which are among several EAS products now approved by virtue of having been certified/approved under the NFL/NFLPA Supplement Label Certification Program after training), to aid in promoting optimal recovery.

178

In terms of the cardio approach, the Body-*for*-LIFE endorsed HIIT (High Intensity Interval Training) approach should be just what the doctor ordered for maximizing both time and the resulting benefit of creating a post-exercise "fat burning" effect long after the actual session is over. Of course those of you who wish to instead perform periodic lower-intensity and longer duration cardio training (to either demonstrate or enhance endurance) are free to do so. Enjoy both aspects of these approaches. As mentioned earlier, both pre-and post-workout nutrition are very real concerns with a quick-acting carbohydrate and quality protein drink to be consumed immediately following an intense (HIIT) cardio training session, while after a low/moderate (less intense) cardio approach, you could simply instead, consume a quality whole-food meal shortly following your training.

Stretching, thought of as one of the staples of fitness, (along with strength and cardiovascular fitness) is an often controversial subject. First, there are multiple applications and techniques such as Ballistic stretching, Dynamic stretching, Active and Passive stretching, as well as Static stretching (confused yet?). Secondly, the topic has, as of late, simply come under a lot of scrutiny in terms of it's effectiveness when used as part of a pre-workout strategy. Some strength coaches and trainers feel that excessive stretching prior to the session will actually hinder power performance in the gym or on the practice and playing field, while others still emphasize it's importance "pre-workout" to offset injury and increase muscle "readiness". For example, martial artists place an extreme emphasis on flexibility and proper stretching, which may help to properly align the skeleton and ease joint compression. Yoga practitioners rely on the importance of stretching and flexibility to help create a harmony and balance with their chosen art.

Although the debate over pre-performance stretching continues, it is generally agreed upon universally that stretching following the workout (while the muscles and/or joint areas are warm and more pliable) provides the safest and greatest benefit to enhance one's flexibility and possible injury prevention. A safe approach to stretching (consider stretching any muscle group only after it is warm and more pliable) is to first raise the body's core temperature with an activity such as mild/moderate walking, jogging, etc. Gently move into the stretch position(s) and hold (no bouncing) the position for upwards of 30 seconds. Relax and repeat several times. You will find that more frequent stretching throughout the day will be more beneficial then periodic and haphazard attempts to increase flexibility.

No matter where you stand in terms of defining the value and benefit of pre-workout stretching/flexibility, it's my guess that everyone can benefit from incorporating a safe, consistent post-workout stretch protocol.

NOW !, If you are willing to work with proper intensity, you may be actually able to maintain (remember, that's merely maintain) an acceptable level of fitness with as few as 2 resistance training sessions coupled with 2 cardio-component sessions per week. You should still keep a journal of your exercise sessions-You can't just guess at your level of performance. You still are striving to compete hard against yourself.

One example of a 4 day per week maintenance phase plan is as follows;

Schedule A- Legs, Chest, Triceps, Abdominals

Schedule B- Cardio only

Schedule C- Back, Shoulders, Biceps, Abdominals.

Schedule D- Cardio only

This could, for instance, incorporate a "2 days on, 1 day off," "2 days on, 2 days off approach" as listed below.

Day 1- Schedule A

Day 2- Schedule B

Day 3- Off

Day 4- Schedule C

Day 5- Schedule D

Day 6- Off

Day 7- Off

A great idea to offset boredom and predictability with this "fitness thing" approach is to find an alternate activity (or two) that can be integrated or combined with the Body-*for-*LIFE training lifestyle. Consider playing pickup basketball a few evenings per week. Maybe take up some form of martial arts as a rewarding hobby, play flag football or slow-pitch softball. You can rollerblade, attend cycling/spinning classes, or enjoy the out-of-doors with hiking, or form a jogging club. Find something you can look forward to, and go for it ! Part of the reward of your new and improved body is to be able to use it more efficiently somewhere other than just in the gym.

It is no doubt that one of life's true pleasures is eating. There are obviously endless delicious foods, recipes, and meals that can be enjoyed by everyone. The sad part is that most of us gravitate toward the most convenient and abundant foods-in most cases that means "fast food" and empty-calorie snacks. This is where you must make the decision to be in control. No one says that you shouldn't indulge in some "forbidden" foods once in a while. Life should never be so "Spartan-like" that any periodic enjoyment of your favorite treat is strictly out of the question. Who wants to live like that? Instead, realize that by making better choices with food and meal planning, your daily performances in and out of the gym, at work, and at play will benefit from loading better "fuel in your tank", so to speak. You have heard it before-"You are what you eat". We have also heard "You are what you think". Those two statements are tightly woven together. If, for some reason, you don't think that the only body you will ever have is worthy of quality fuel, then maybe it's time to rethink! While one meal won't make you "fit or fat," it is those choices and actions (wise or unwise) we all make day after day, week after week, month after month, and year after year that help to mold us into who we will eventually become.

Luckily there are great meal and food choice selections found in such books as Body-*for*-LIFE and Eating-*for*-LIFE, as two examples. Many of us live life at a frantic pace. That's still no excuse for not relying on wise whole food and/or meal alternative choices while trying "to touch all the nutritional bases". Handy meal replacement powders (MRP's), such as Myoplex and convenient nutritional bars such as the new EAS Body-*for*-LIFE Balanced Nutrition Bars are perfect choices whether you are someone "on the go", or simply want affordable (and again), convenient alternatives to standing in a slow moving line, or having to sit too long in a crowded restaurant with little time to spare.

By now you are aware of the overall food choices that make up a healthy plan for nutritional balance. Let's go over it once more-Favorable carbohydrates such as oatmeal, sweet potatoes and yams, brown rice, whole wheat pasta, whole grain breads, beans, etc., are examples of staple foods for long term energy, coupled with wise protein choices (tissue repair)-egg whites, chicken, turkey, fish, lean red meat, lowfat cottage cheese, skim and lowfat milk and of course the inclusion of "good" fats-- almonds, walnuts, avocado, and natural peanut butter to list a few, as well as the use of favorable oils (Flaxseed Oil, Olive Oil, Safflower Oil, Canola Oil, and Borage Oil). Not to be forgotten are vegetables and most fruits (for both fiber and anti-oxidant value). All of these selections will provide vital nutrients to meet the daily requirements for both the professional athlete, as well as the needs of most people who are simply seeking to feel better and to be better.

On dozens of bookshelves in every bookstore, and even glaring at you while you stand in the check-out line in your local supermarket, are countless diet books, dietary approaches and sure-fire nutritional remedies guaranteed to "fix that weight problem". Some are "fad" approaches, while others are quite good--based on sound principles and sprinkled with a dose of common sense. Hate to sound repetitive, but try to select a variety of nutritious foods that are high in fiber, are adequate in quality protein, and those carbohydrate selections that provide longer, more sustained energy. You should constantly avoid hydrogenated oils (found in baked goods, margarine and chips) and also seek some good fats (those low in saturated fat) daily, which can include vegetable oils, nuts, avocado, seeds and cold water fish, such as salmon.

Now comes the part a lot of us (both guys and gals) seem to dread-the actual preparation of the meal. Luckily, there are options for folks who aren't quite ready to compete with the experts found on "The Food Channel ". Below find some easy –to- prepare alternatives;

· Healthy wraps and tortillas
· MRP's (Myoplex - a "meal in a pouch")
· Nutritious sandwiches on whole grain breads coupled with a piece of fresh fruit.
· Hearty soups and whole wheat crackers.
· Fat-free yogurt with an added scoop of protein powder.

184

· Low-fat cottage cheese and a fruit selection.

An example of an "easy- to- follow" meal plan may look like this: (remember, smaller, more frequent meals are still preferred)

Meal 1- An egg white omelet/with lowfat cheese and green peppers, and a bowl of oatmeal.

Meal 2- A tuna sandwich on whole grain bread and an apple.

Meal 3- A grilled chicken salad, sprinkled with slivered almonds.

Meal 4- An MRP (meal replacement powder- Myoplex , for example) or an EAS Body-*for*-LIFE Balanced Nutrition Bar.

Meal 5- Salmon filet, or a lean ground beef patty, a small serving of brown rice and 2 vegetable selections.

Meal 6- A small serving of lowfat cottage cheese w/ berries or grapes.

If time is the issue and meal 2 or 3 is out of the question, substitute a RTD (Body-*for*-LIFE Ready-to-Drink Shake or EAS Nutritional Bar). It takes exactly 2.1 seconds to open either choice. Don't skip or miss your meals.

What about periodic "snacks"? 'Gotta have my snacks! There are lots of healthy and convenient choices. Unsalted peanuts, air-popped popcorn, fruit, non-fat yogurt, non-fat frozen yogurt, whole grain wheat crackers and/or celery with natural peanut butter serve as just a few examples.

You probably didn't have to look too hard to see that there were no cheeseburgers, pizza, cheesecake or ice cream listed anywhere. Now wait just one minute! How about a few cold beers or a glass or two of wine once in a while? Well, we said this thing should never be so sacrificial that we can't enjoy some of those "pleasures of the palette" from time to time. Of course you can! Just don't make the easy mistake of letting those "pleasure foods" make up the majority of your nutrition, and then only once-in-a-while eat wisely with good health and improved performance in mind. If you have been successful in completing this Challenge, then you know you've worked hard to get to where you are. You deserve to be rewarded and certainly you deserve to "indulge" periodically. Please don't self-destruct by "way of fork."

Dining out is typically a pleasurable experience. Dining out with friends is even more enjoyable. Each time Porter makes it back home to Orlando, Florida, we go out and "put on the feed bag"---and for the most part, we do it wisely. Several of the restaurants we always frequent (Ruby Tuesday's comes to mind) are always more than willing to accomodate each request for healthy and nutritious meals.They even make the effort to supply the patron with a nutritional value review on their menu items. It's great to to be able to really "have it your way".

Maintaining anything of value is really all about balance.

"Balancing" relies on discipline, focus, purpose, attitude, enthusiasm, passion, priority-- well, those of you who have done the 84 days know far better than most about a lifestyle balance. Just remember who you have now become, and hopefully will want to remain. The decision has always been yours.

I hope this section and the entire book has given you the "wake up call" to a healthier Life. If I can answer a specific question about your getting healthy or if there is any confusion about becoming more fit, please feel free to contact me.

Train Smart,
Eric Shrieves
www.finallyfit.net
Orlando, Florida
407-894-4601

—Appendix B—

A Few thoughts...

The nice folks at EAS were kind enough to let me re-print a couple of my Freeman's Word articles from the past few years. Mind you some of my opinions and views didn't get past the editors (or at least the way I expressed them) but non the less, a right good portion of them did make it!

What they lacked in punctuation and correct grammar, they made up for in honesty. Sometimes brutal honesty, as if there is any other kind. The magazine I wrote for is gone. As you know by now the Body-*for*-LIFE and EAS are in 64 countries and sometimes translating Freeman's Word lost a little something in Greek or German or Spanish. Hell, sometimes it lost a little something getting translated in English.

Anyway here we go....a few of the 50 or 60 Freeman's Word articles. Some brought a smile or frown or sometimes a tear. Regardless they all had a message and still do. Hope one of them speaks to you, it will be just like the two of us are talking.

188

I Slipped

I slipped. That's it, there is nothing else to it, I slipped. It took three years to do it, but it finally happened. Now what do I do? I felt bad about it for a couple of days and finally forgave myself. I'm glad I felt bad. It shows that I still care about what happens to me. Now hundreds of thousands of people that read this magazine know I made a mistake. The question is what am I going to do about it?

Well, the first thing I am going to do is figure out how and why it happened. Perhaps if I know the answer to those two questions, I won't mess up again. Somebody a lot smarter then me said I should identify the problem. Hell, I know what the problem is; I am addicted to food and alcohol. So I am right back where I started, with the "how" it happened. After thinking about how it happened, let me tell you "why" it happened

A few too many cold ones! This leads to ordering a rack of grease dripping barbecued pork ribs, the large order, of course. A few more cold ones and well, what the heck, I'm here, I might as well have a large pork sandwich. I wasn't driving that night so I had a few more cold ones. It was great. I have made some new friends out here in Colorado and there was a real nice lady there that night and she was laughing and having a cold one and I was laughing and having a cold one and she was eating a big plate of New Orleans gumbo and she was real pretty and boy oh boy, I had a few more cold ones and that's how it happened.

Where was my nutritional program? I didn't take it with me that night. Why did I order all those cold ones and willingly eat 100 grams of pure fat? I think it was because, although I left my nutritional program at home, my old friend, addiction, showed up that night and joined me. So how did it happen? I figured out how it happened, simple, I was in the wrong place. Like the donut store, I just do not have any business in a restaurant where I can see, smell, and hear barbecue cooking. I put in my face what I shouldn't be doing. That's how it happened.

Why did it happen? It was so innocent. I had a date, we were going to see a local blues band and we stopped real quick to get a bite to eat. The place is here in Denver and they get real serious about their barbecue. I should have turned around at the door but I didn't. Why? Because the smell of that food, mixed with the smell of her perfume and the thought of a cold one before some hard blues, it all got me! I didn't have a chance. I could say it was my free day and get away with it but that would be a lie. I use my free day to stay on the program. There is nothing that says I have to do everything bad on my free day. Granted, a cold beer once in a while isn't the end of the world. If I want one, ever now and then, I can have one, same thing with the barbecue. Problem is, I had enough that night to hold me over till Thanksgiving 2006.

Now, I know how and why it happened. I'm not going to give up the blues, I'm not going to give up on the girl, but I might have to give up going down the street that restaurant is on. I know I went to the wrong place and I know why, I better watch that, or it will get me in trouble. I don't want to backslide to where I used to be.

If you are like me and have made a mistake, it isn't the end of the world. We should both be sorry we messed up and try not to do it again. We are human and humans make errors. I am back on

190

course this week. I won't be going anywhere near, those things that got me sidetracked last week. I hope you don't either. Remember Bill said, "fail fast", he didn't say fail forever. Do not stop because you slip. Do not stay down and accept defeat because of a mistake. It is not defeat; it is just a mistake, nothing more.

I plan to succeed with this Body-*for*-LIFE. I promised a lot of people, I would. The one person who is counting on me the most is "me". I made a mistake, I admitted it, and now I have to move on. I forgave myself. You need to do the same if you have slipped. We all have, we are not alone. Get up, try not to do it again, pick right up where you left off and complete the twelve weeks. I'm proud of you, and I hope you are still proud of me. I will try to not slip again, if I do, please offer me a helping hand, I would do it for you.

Good News

A few weeks back a gentleman called EAS with some questions concerning the Body-*for*-LIFE Challenge. As usual the courteous people that answer the phones here gave him ample information and good advice. All was well. Before he hung up he ask if it was possible to talk to me for a minute? Of course it was. I happened to be in my office and they patched him through. I'm never too busy to talk to anyone; I'm just not here often.

We had a good talk and I honestly enjoyed hearing the enthusiasm in his voice. He had the Body-*for*-LIFE book and he had seen the videos and he now knew what supplements best suited him and he had only one little concern, one issue that had been bothering him for a year or two. He was being honest

191

when he said he didn't want to be all bulked up and look like those people on stage all swelled up and such! Well friend, I had "Great" news for him, it was his lucky day; there was no chance this side of China that he would ever look like those swelled up people on stage.

I have heard reasons and excuses of every kind why someone doesn't get healthy. I've listen to people tell me flat out that they love the couch and wouldn't go to the gym if they got paid to go. Fair enough, nobody "has" to get healthy. But, if anyone reading this thinks a 12-week one time Body-*for*-LIFE program is going to qualify them for the Mr. Olympia, that would be that same as believing if you played a flag football game, you are going to knock Emmett Smith out of a job.

Listen.... we have met and known a few professional bodybuilders and they all report it takes years of discipline and dedication and sacrifice to come near being on the stage as a professional. The men and women you see in top-level bodybuilding competitions were not couch potatoes 3 months ago. They take training and nutrition and rest to a level I am not capable of. Maybe you can do it but I neither could nor want to.

The Body-*for*-LIFE is a livable doable rewarding life style. It's Life Building, not body building. Building your body is a wonderful result of improving your Life. Granted you might have to buy some new cloths and you will definitely have to buy a new bathing suit. Yes, you will have to listen to co-workers ask why you are looking so good and you might even have people flirt with you that never noticed you before the 12 weeks. All those things could and probably will happen. But in the 6 years that I have been here, we have never had one Challenger call and complain that they got too big and are all bulked up now and nobody likes them. That dog don't hunt! He will have to find a better excuse to stay unhealthy...

I have a lot of respect for the men and women who go on stage and compete. They hide nothing. They are out there for the audience to see and judge and they have to be in pretty good shape to qualify. Just to walk out there and be under the lights makes them a Champion in their own right. You cannot send in pictures in that competition, you have to show up and be seen. Want to get into amateur or professional bodybuilding; the Body-*for*-LIFE is a good place to start. Want to get into Life; the Body-*for*-LIFE is a good place to Live. No more excuses.

A Little Rain Must Fall

No one I know is immune from a dose of hardship in his or her life. It really doesn't matter who we are or who we think we are, nature has an uncanny way of bringing a little rain our way. Hopefully it's only a summer shower and not a Texas flood.

There is no way to compare the daily inconveniences of a dead battery or a missed bus with some of the tragedies we, as a country, have experienced in the last few years. I heard about a gym closing in the middle of the night and the members found an empty building the next morning. Granted that is wrong and an inconvience but should that be the end of your fitness program? I think not. It's just a little rain.

Bum Phillips the former coach of the Houston Oilers is credited with saying, "There are 2 kinds of coaches in the NFL, them that's been fired and them that's gonna be." I think his philosophy is on target. The day we come screaming into this world, we are due some good times and some bad. The Chinese martial artiest believe in the yen and the yang, you don't know good if you don't know bad. If everything were constantly wonderful in your Life how would you know it? You would have nothing to compare wonderful with. Maybe that's not a bad idea but it isn't going to happen.

Have you had your heart broken? I sure have. I was miserable until I realized there were only about 6 billion people on this earth and half of them are girls! That's 3 billion chances I have of meeting someone else. Not bad odds.

Let's review. If your gym closed or you lost your job or your sweetheart left you, it isn't the end of the world. Pick yourself up and keep moving. There is a world of difference in a broken heart and one that has stopped! I don't believe there is a silver lining behind every cloud; I do think it will eventually quit raining. If it doesn't, we should build an ark.

Nobody wants to lose their job (I sure don't) but you had one before you got the one your at now. Somebody will hire you. Understand that people are at some point going to let you down. Whether you get up again is your choice, not theirs. How far you get up is also your choice, not theirs. We get one Father and one Mother, which is very important. What we drive isn't important. Never, ever confuse wealth with worth; they are two completely different things. Finally but most importantly is your health. What could possible be more important then your health and your family and their health? Nothing!

194

I had a bad day and wrote this article. It wouldn't matter if I wrote it or David Kennedy wrote it or Ryan Mattingly or the man in the moon wrote it, as long as the message comes across. A year from now it won't matter which bachlorette was chosen, it won't matter whose tribe won or who got kicked off the island. What will matter is if we have lived out the year and if we have improved our quality of Life. If our lives are not moving forward, we can only be going in one other direction, and that is backwards. Don't go backwards, keep improving each day, if you fall, don't stay down; there won't be anywhere else to go.

Concerning next year, our health is a good place to start, because that's where we are going to finish. Trust me, it ends at a hospital, not the bank.

It Seemed Like a Normal Day

It seemed like a normal day. Up early, aerobics, healthy breakfast, shower, and out the door. Arrive at work, morning pleasantries, a second cup of coffee and go about my daily business. (Still can't believe I work here) Around 10:30a.m. I have a short break and wander in the employee kitchen , mix a Myoplex lite and scan a discarded newspaper. There it is on the front page. It is no longer just a normal day, it's Veterans Day.

When I think about how I got in such bad shape 3 years ago, I can't get away from the fact, that my state of health was a direct result of the choices I was making. I, along with everybody else in America, had and still have, the freedom of choice to be fit and healthy, or unfit and unhealthy. It dawned on me that choice was bought and paid for by hundreds of thousands of honorable and noble men and women. In a word Veterans.

There is a wonderful scene in the movie "Full Metal Jacket" where a overweight recruit, gets to eat a jelly donut, while all the other recruits pay for it, by doing push-ups. America has thousands of men and women, who are ready and willing on a moment's notice to pay the price for the rest of us to have all the jelly donuts we want. We can have all the fat drenched junk food we want. We can wash it down with gallons of beer and soda pop. If my memory is correct, I finished it all off with a half a gallon of pecan ice cream. Why not, somebody else was paying for it.

One night, standing in front of the Steel Mill Gym, I noticed the gym is located between a small grocery store and a neighborhood pub. The little store has chips and candies and soda and all that kind of stuff. The neighborhood pub has all the other kinds of stuff. As I walked toward the front door of the gym, it crossed my mind that there was about 50 feet between each door. A hundred feet separate 3 doors, but the results of the door I chose were about a million miles apart. None the less, the choice was mine and that " right to choose" was paid for 225 years ago and is being defended as you read this article.

Sometimes we get a letter from another country explaining how difficult it is to be healthy. Forget about trying to decide which gym to join, there are people in this world who would give anything for a set of weights. We have many gyms to choose from and so many membership plans and believe me, there are countries where you could find a Ferris wheel sooner then you could find a health club. We have "personal trainers" and lunch buffets. We have health food stores and hundreds of supplements to choose from. They have very little to eat and the only "personal trainers" they come into contact with are the milita, and then it's very personal. I had the priviledge of talking to Sgt. David Kennedy, our 1998 Co-Champion, when he returned from Kosovo. He reported he had to use milk cartons filled with water for weights. His squad would scavenge for any material available to build a make shift workout area. The only supplements were the Myoplex bars we sent him. Why would anyone think the health industry improved when we left that country? It didn't.

Let me take this time to publicly apologize to each and every Veteran, who gave me the right to choose my health. I am sorry for the years I threw away, being unhealthy. I promise I will never abuse the rights and freedoms that you gave me again. I wish I could personally thank each one of you. Duke Dearing, who fought and bled for our freedom. Bob Parmenter, Ron Hill, Harvey Miller, Joe Hendricks, Joe Getherall, Chip Bellamy, Juan Vigil, Don Palko, Nathan Rose, Nick, Randy, Jim, Kathy, Sharon, Adam, Bob, Cameron, Scott, Roy, Gene, Randy, Jeff, Chuck, Doug and Butch, my Dad and his Dad. It is impossible to name all the Veterans, in this limited space. What can be done, is for you to tell the Vets you know, "Thank You" If you know a Vet who has let themselves slip into poor health, remind them of how fit they were when they got out of bootcamp. If you or someone you love is in poor health, because they choose to be, remind them of the debt we owe to all Veterans. You might ask "Why do we owe them anything, it's our health, we can do whatever we want." I guess the answer is like that donut, go ahead and eat it, it's already been paid for.

What I felt this Veterans Day, wasn't pride or flag-waving patriotism, it was guilt, plain and simple. Everything we are is directly related to being free. We have the choice of health or poor health, because a price was paid for it. I abused that choice for a long time. I was wrong. If you are a veteran, or not, and have found yourself in poor health, drop us a line and we will try our best to get you back on the road to good health. There is no charge for the information other then a stamp. I'll be waiting to hear from you.

The Body-*for*-LIFE is 12 weeks. That's 84 days, the same amount of time as boot camp. You made it back then; you can make it now. You have earned the right to be healthy and in the Body-*for*-LIFE, there is a free day every 7th day. The other good news is you do not have to march and we have Success Coaches instead of friendly, smiling Drill Instructors encouraging you.

Thank you veterans, thank you for all our choices. We would not be here today if it were not for all of you. The freedom I have to write this article, the choice to be in good health or poor health, what we eat and drink, whether we exercise today or not, all available because we are free. Please take advantage of the freedoms you have made available. Some places poor health is not a choice, but a way of life. Because of you, that is not the case in America. Whatever choice you make concerning your health will be all right, but please, please make the right choice.

Thank you for all of this, from all of us.

Ride Ends

You just can't live life over again, you just can't. We get one ride on this earth and when it stops, it stops forever. I wish more then anything I could go back to another time in my life and start again. It isn't going to happen. So, how can we change the one ride we get? I think the answer is; we make this ride the absolute ride of a lifetime. That's exactly what it is.

A New Year is upon us and we will get 365 more chances to relocate on the lifetime ride. We can move anywhere on this ride we want to. We can sit by a window seat and watch everything go by, or we can sit in the luggage compartment and not even be aware of the trip. Another option is to get in the driver's seat and direct this ride anywhere we want it to go. We can ride alone or we can go with someone or even in a group. The choice is entirely up to us.

What would you give to back time up? I cannot begin to tell you what all I would do different. It is impossible to go back to yesterday or the day before, or last week or last month or last year. We can change the future. We now get 365 more opportunities, to either sit in the same spot next year, talking about being motivated and getting a grip on our health, or we get up right now and do something about it. What is stopping us? We are. If we do not get up and do something about our lives, the ride goes on regardless and we can continue to sit in the baggage car or we can go up front and drive this train. Be assured the ride goes on either way.

That is how I have started looking at this Life adventure. I know, being 55, that sooner or later this all ends for both of us. There is nothing we can do about the time we have wasted; it is just gone forever. If you are reading this article, you have already shown an interest in improving your health. It is a guarantee that improved health equals an improved Life. Mine did and so did about 1,000,000 others.

It took me 14 years to get out of 12 grades but I have come up with an undeniable mathematic equation. I'm sure my 8th grade algebra teacher is running down the hall screaming at this very moment. Here it is: Rge>DBB-WW: LL! This all stands for "Rides gonna end, Don't Be Baggage-Watching from the Window, Live Life". I might tape that up on my wall. It's simple and to the point and I like it. I don't ever want to be baggage again, sitting in the dark, having Life push me along. I don't want to sit by the window and watch everyone else live Life, I want to take charge and continue Living Life. The ride is definitely going to end; I want us to do our best to enjoy ever how-many miles we have left.

Running

Almost all the exercise routines in the world call for some sort of cardiovascular activity. We will call this "cardio" for short. In order to change and improve our bodies we have to follow a good nutritional program, perform some level of resistance training and do our cardio.

There is an abundance of cardio activities to choose from. We can swim, pedal a real or stationary bike, skip rope, shadow box, spin, dance, climb stairs or any number of other exercises. This year I was invited to go skiing and snow shoeing. Since we didn't get a lot of snow when I lived in Florida, I wasn't very good at it but my friend was patient and I caught on real fast. I appreciate her taking me. If you want to talk about a good cardio exercise, go snow shoeing. I was worn out! The one exercise I haven't mentioned is probably the most popular: running. I hate to run. My back hurts, my knees hurt, my ankles hurt and I give out of breath. The problem is, with no other cardio equipment available, you can always run.

There has to be a simple way to make running a little less painful. On a visit to my Chiropractor, Dr. Shawn Caldwell I asked for some tips and would like to share them with you. He has been an athlete all his life and running is part of his weekly workouts. Dr. Caldwell explained: Running involves the "closed kinematics chain". What that means is the foot; ankle, knee, hip, pelvis and back are all connected. If something goes wrong in your ankle, then the results can appear in your hip. There may be nothing wrong with your hip but the pain is manifest there. Add to this the fact that running forces 3 times your weight on impact to your foot. A 200-pound man (due to impact) is exerting 600 pounds of pressure on each foot when it hits the ground.

Well, what should we do to improve our comfort and decrease the odds of an injury while running? Dr. Caldwell suggested the following 4 options:

1. Select two good pairs of running shoes. We all have different strides and each time we run we hit the ground in our same pattern. This can cause "overuse syndrome". With two pairs of running shoes we automatically change the impact point and give our feet a break every other workout.

2. Select the softest running surface to start. Begin running on grass, then a rubber running tract, dirt, asphalt, or cement.

On a side note let me urge you to walk the grass part first so you don't step in a hole like I did! There must be a lot of gophers in Colorado.

3. Have a professional evaluate the integrity of your arches. Arches are shock absorbers that disperse the impact of your weight coming down on your foot. If the arch has fallen the impact is now transferred up the "kinematics chain" and creates problems in other joints or structures above. Abnormal arches should be adjusted to correct degrees or if needed support orthotics introduced.

4. Evaluate both legs to discover any discrepancy in length. (I think what he means is if one leg is shorter then the other). There are two types of short legs: functional and anatomical. Functional can possible be treated with realignment of the joints. Anatomical is an abnormal growth of the actual bone. This condition may be treated with orthotics or heal lifts. All 4 areas should be addressed before anyone begins a running routine.

I also asked Dr. Jeanette Y. Kelder D.C. if there was any specific advice she could offer women that begin a running routine. Dr. Kelder is an outstanding athlete and stays in excellent health year round. She was involved in soccer, volleyball and track during her high school and college days. Today Dr. Kelder plays on 2 volleyball teams and runs 2 or 3 times a week. She agrees with Dr. Caldwell and adds you should always warm up and do some stretching exercises before running. It doesn't matter if it is a short sprint or a long haul, stretch and warm up first. She advises hydrating your body through out the day to avoid cramping during your workouts. Now where have we heard that before?

It probably sounds like common sense but dress for comfort when doing your cardio running routine. Don't wear cloths that are tight and interfere with your circulation and don't be stopping every other block to pull your pants and socks up. Maybe she has watched me run. Probably the best advice I heard was stop if you really feel a sharp pain or nausea. I understand there may be some discomfort, but to run to an injury is self-destructive.

Both Dr. Caldwell and Dr. Kelder practice what they preach. They are in great health, neither of them smokes or abuse alcohol and both routinely exercise and follow an intelligent nutritional program. I thank them for helping me with this article.

I don't know if making these changes will improve my dislike for running but I do know I will be more comfortable. I also know there will be less chance of an injury and being set back in my training. Everyone in the Body-*for*-LIFE Challenge has to do some sort of cardio exercise. Find the one that suits you and is available for you. If there isn't a bike or punching bag or swimming pool available, start running. Listen to the good Doctors and follow their advice. I'm going to try it their way and see what happens.

The Process

The process of physical "self-reinvention" is far too valuable to casually attempt. Each and every workout really represents the ultimate game, the World Series, the Super Bowl, the Stanley Cup. We cannot have a series of, or even a few, non-productive sessions in the gym and expect to achieve our best final results. Our ultimate achievements reflect the sum total of the most productive and focused efforts in the gym.

There is no room for a sub-par season. We are not the NBA where .500 for the season might earn us a play off spot. We cannot sit out 40% of the season and return to hit the winning home run in game 7 of the World Series. Each workout is as important as the next and our Championship season is ultimately determined by a series of productive sessions. Unfortunately it isn't the Rocky Balboa story. We don't get the luxury of being mediocre, haphazard and then in a final effort, win the "belt."

Every workout, every rep, every set, should be our best effort. The sum total from each attempt will result in the finished product-our best bodies! Keep that in mind when hitting the gym. We never have a chance for the same workout again. Good or bad, the last workout you did is over and the results are in. Do your best each and every time. Train smart.

Okay folks, there it is. It's a workout, work and get out! Go to the gym or basement or garage or wherever you train, leave all your troubles at the door in a sack and focus on the task at hand. This has been called a thousand things: Mind Body Connection, Focus, Zen-the list is endless but the message is the same. Think about what you are doing in the gym. Think about what sculpture and shape you are trying to achieve. Trust me, all our problems will be right where we left them when the workout is over.

Our lives have good and bad days. All of us are going to experience roadblocks and obstacles along the way, that is just the way it is. But, when you do get in the gym and when you do have 45 minutes to workout and train, drop fat, gain muscle and zero in on what you are doing. You hit the bull's-eye when you make the effort to aim. Make getting in the gym a priority and when you are in there make the time and effort count. If you don't, then it is a waste of time. We can hardly afford to waste one minute on anything. I have never thought the gym was a social event. It isn't about being seen or seeing who is in there. It isn't about the latest gym fashion or the newest hairstyle. Go in, clear your mind, work on your body and accomplish something before you walk out the door. I promise your social life will improve after you have done the work, not while you are doing it.

Freeman's Word

I don't get to read the paper much but I did catch one recent interesting article. If I have my facts right, there is a gentleman in New York who is suing a couple of fast food restaurants because he gained a lot of weight and had some heart problems. That gave me a great idea. I am going to sue the Doctor that delivered me because one day I am going to die. Surely he can be held responsible to some degree for my ageing and deteriorating body. Don't you agree?

Maybe I could do a class action suit and include my Grandmothers and both my parents. They loaded me up with fried chicken and biscuits and strawberry shortcake when I was a little boy. Hold on, I just thought of something. I will include the people who made the spoons that dug into the ice cream I crammed down my throat from the first grade through 1997. Now we're really on to something. Maybe a sharp lawyer can prove the music being played by the ice-cream truck was like the pied piper and his flute. As a child I would hear that jingle and nothing could stop me from running to the sound of that music and parting with my dime in exchange for a cone of vanilla. I believe the ice cream man drove a Ford but I couldn't swear it in court. We will simply have to subpoena all the ice cream truck records from 1955.

Look, if you poke a stick of dynamite in your mouth and light it, more then likely it will blow your head off. But, nowhere on the label does it say, "Do not eat". Are we going to need to put a warning on all the things that will hurt us if we are incapable of having a little self control and even less common since? I got a cavity in the 3rd grade so it is my constitutional right to sue all the people who gave me Halloween candy.

If we can sue the tobacco companies for lung related diseases, then we should be able to sue the liquor industry for liver disease and all the alcohol related deaths and destruction alcohol abuse causes each day, month and year. The key word here is "ABUSE". A single smoke isn't going to kill you. A single drink of alcohol isn't going to kill you. A single fast food serving isn't going to kill you. Remember, can't buy smokes if you are under 18, you will get in a lot of trouble if you drink and drive or have a few drinks and play with guns but, there is no age limits or food police when it comes to stuffing your face. What I know to be the truth is this; I was on my way to an early grave when I had no self-control and a total lack of common since about forcing massive amounts of junk into my body. It is legal to make sugar. It is utter stupidity to eat 29 pounds of cotton candy for lunch. Get it?

Say, come to think of it, my eyes have been bothering me for the last few years and I have had to start wearing reading glasses. As I wrote this Freeman's word it dawned on me why. I think I will add Hugh Hefner to my list of people to be sued. For years he has contributed to the wear and tear and strain on my eyes. Surely he can be held responsible to some degree, don't you think?

Thank you to a few more people.

At the end of this book I was thinking about some of the people who have really added to my value as a person. I was thinking about the Police Departments where I have spoken and met some of America's finest. There are a lot of good people out there and here are a few of them.

The Tucson Police Department
Phyllis Williams, Paul Patterson.

The Cincinnati Police Department
Todd Bruner
The Denver Police Department
Joe Bini. Chief Gerald Whitman

North Miami Beach Police Department
Nelson Reyes

Jackson Wyoming Police Department
Tampa Police Department
Chief Bennie Holder

Utah Valley State College
Public Safety Chief Tracy Marrott

Woodville Texas Police Department
Chief Scott Yosko

New Orleans Police Department
Chief Edwin Compass, Lt. Kevin Anderson

Jefferson County Sheriff Office Colorado
Sheriff Ted Mink

Jefferson County Deputies
Leslie Hamblin and Rich Brooks, Sgt. Grant Whitus...
Thank You! (my Department)

Johnson County Sheriff Office Kansas
Lt. Casey Wilder
Wichita Police Department
Sgt. Darren Chambers

You met Steve Grossi from the PAPD, let me include Miguel
Rivera NYPD

Hackensack Police Department
Lt. Donald Pierce

Policia De Puerto Rico
Insp. Anibal Marrero Rosa

Golden Police Department
Gino DePalma

The list goes on a long way. We have presented at The IRS Criminal Investigation Division, ICE, Homeland Security, and the new Sky Marshals Office in the Western section of America. I can't put names with the Federal Departments for the obvious reason but, the men and women of these Departments know what a Honor it was for us to be allowed to visit and train with them.

I told the Sky Marshals their motto should be "Two places at once" They are our first line of defense and our last hope at the same time.

Thank you to Bill McGahee, Tom Fuller, Tracie Jeffries and Ana Canton, they know why. The more I sit here the longer this list will become. I have to thank Shane Thomas and Marc Bennett. They actually run the Body-*for*-LIFE Challenge, I am again just the messenger. Thank you all, Porter.

Jim Schneeberger with 60 pounds of equipment, trying to become a Selous Scout

Double-time up the hill. The "quitters truck" was always there in the background. Jim didn't quit.

Selous Scout calf workout

Selous Scout rope workout

Scout candidate carries an 80 pound box with no handles. You had to want it!

More rope training. The safety net is thorn bushes

The finish to Jim's 12-week challenge

Duke Dearing, Drill Instructor, teaching a new recruit to be a Marine

Outside DaNang early 1970's

Squared Away

Some of Hugh "Duke" Dearing's medals

Porter with Tampa Bay
Police Chief
Bennie Holder

Porter with New Orleans
Police Chief Edwin Compass

Eric Shrieves training
Body-*for*-LIFE runner-up
Champion Lynn Oglesby

Eric and Lynn
following the
program

Eric and Porter after the Night of the Champions
in Golden, Colorado, 1997

Eric with Cindy Streich and Porter.
Cindy graduated from the Body-*for*-LIFE
Transformation Camp in Golden